NORTH TO THULE

JOHN AND HARRIET FRYE

NORTH TO THULE

AN IMAGINED NARRATIVE OF THE
FAMOUS "LOST" SEA VOYAGE OF PYTHEAS OF
MASSALIA IN THE FOURTH CENTURY B.C.

Illustrations by Harriet Frye

ALGONQUIN BOOKS OF CHAPEL HILL
1985

ALGONQUIN BOOKS OF CHAPEL HILL
Post Office Box 2225
Chapel Hill, North Carolina 27515-2225

Library of Congress Cataloging in Publication Data
Frye, John, 1910–
North to Thule.

Bibliography: p.
1. Pytheas, of Massalia–Fiction. 2. Greece–History–To 146 B.C.–Fiction. 3. Europe, Northern–Discovery and exploration–Greek–Fiction. I. Frye, Harriet. II. Title
PS3556.R93N6 1985 813'.54 84-28236

ISBN 0-912697-20-2
Printed in the United States of America

CONTENTS

ILLUSTRATIONS AND MAPS

ILLUSTRATIONS

MAPS

THE BEGINNING

THIS IS A STORY of how a great voyage of exploration might have been made more than two millennia ago. It must be an imagined chronicle. All we know is what a few men had to say about it before the original record disappeared more than thirteen centuries ago.

It is about a questing man who may have been the first from the Inner Sea cradle of civilization to come to or near an unknown land he named Thule, somewhere in the North Atlantic Ocean.

The man was Pytheas (Pie-*thay*-as), astronomer and geographer of the Greek colony city of Massalia, now France's Mediterranean port of Marseille. Most scholars agree his voyage was made in the fourth century B.C., probably about the time of Alexander the Great and the latter's boyhood tutor Aristotle.

Of Pytheas we know nothing – young or old, slim or fat, bald or hairy, benedict or bachelor – not even with certainty whether he was a sea captain and navigator or a scientist-passenger on another man's ship – in today's idiom, "principal investigator." About the philosopher-scientist Aristotle and the conqueror-king Alexander we have endless detail. They left records and deeds.

Pytheas was not inarticulate, nor secretive like the Phoenician and Carthaginian traders who told little of what they learned about the world, especially its riches. Nor did he find it unnecessary to put down landfalls and bearings on strange coasts, like the Basque and Breton fishermen who probably saw North American shores decades if not centuries before Christopher Columbus "invented" the ship's log with his *Diario* of his first voyage of discovery.

Pytheas wrote it all in *Peri tou Okeanou,* his *About the Ocean,* for the city elders who had sent him to break the Carthaginian blockade of the Pillars of Herakles, the Strait of Gibraltar, and find original sources for cassiterite – tin – and elektron – amber, fossilized tree resin. Cassiterite, the "white metal," was for alloying copper from Tartessos or Turditania, now southwestern Spain's Andalucía, for bronze for armor, weapons, tools, and utensils in the centuries of the Mediterranean's transition from the Bronze to the Iron Age. Elektron was prized for

Amulets of amber, often shaped as animals, were prized for their "magic" properties because they gave off static electricity when rubbed.

jewelry and decorations, especially if insects or leaves trapped to become fossilized with the resin showed in the pieces. It was even more prized by many for amulets with its "magic"–its property of attracting small objects and human hair when rubbed to create what we now call static electricity.

Cassiterite was believed to come from the Cassiterides, probably England's Scilly Islands, though it actually came from nearby Cornwall, ancient Pou Kernou, with some from northwestern Spain. Most elektron came from an unknown northern land around a gulf known as Metuonis, our Baltic Sea. The Carthaginian blockade of the entrance to the Mediterranean forced both to be hauled by river and pack animals across Keltika, Rome's Gaul and our France, thus thinning the profits of Massaliot merchants. The elektron trade was declining by Pytheas' time but still important on the Mediterranean.

Pytheas' journal was read by many of his own time and later. The historian Timaeus, and Dicaearchus, Aristotle's heir, both of Athens, the astronomer Hipparchus of Rhodes, Eratosthenes, for a half century director of the Library of Alexandria, and Polybius, Strabo, and Pliny the Elder of Rome, quote from it, although indirectly. We cannot. Sometime during two centuries of destruction of the Library of Alexandria, ending in A.D. 640, it was lost. Thus we depend on what was seen by other men, some accepting, others loudly critical.

Among critics, perhaps the loudest was Polybius, a Greek enjoying Roman captivity a century after Pytheas and fancying himself a discoverer and geographer. Ironically, much of Polybius' writing has been lost but its envious contempt for Pytheas has been preserved by Strabo, another Greek living in Rome in the last century B.C. and first A.D., in one of his many volumes on geography. Strabo quotes Polybius freely, including his famous complaint: "How is it possible that a private individual, and one too in narrow circumstances, could ever have performed such vast expeditions by sea and land? And how could Eratosthenes, who hesitates whether he may rely on his statements in general, place such entire confidence in what that writer narrates concerning Britain, Gades and Iberia? It would have been better had Eratosthenes trusted to the Messenian [Evemerus, a now forgotten Sicilian author, contemporary to Pytheas] rather than to this writer. The former merely pretends to have sailed into one [unknown] country, viz. Panchaea, but the latter, that he has visited the whole of the north of Europe, as far as the ends of the earth; which statement, even had it been made by Mercury, we should not have believed."

Strabo endorsed much of Polybius' criticism and added his own epithet, "Pytheas, by whom many have been deceived." He scolded Eratosthenes and Hipparchus for basing parts of their own works on Pytheas' report, and wrote, "It is this last writer who states that he travelled all over Britain on foot, and that the island is above 40,000 stadia in circumference."

Yet he continued with details he, and later Pliny, scorned—but which are so valuable to us now:

"It is likewise he who describes Thule and other neighboring places, where, according to him, neither earth, water, nor air exist, separately,

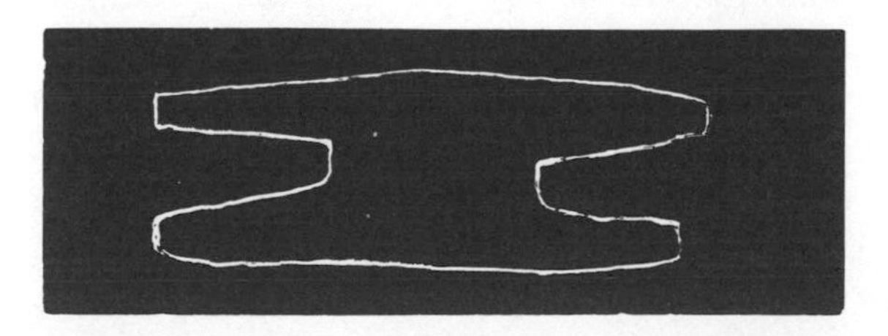

Knucklebone ingot of cassiterite.

but a concretion of all these, resembling marine sponge, in which the earth, the sea, and all things were suspended, thus forming, as it were, a link to unite the whole together. It can neither be travelled over nor sailed through. As for the substance, he affirms that he has beheld it with his own eyes; the rest, he reports on the authority of others. So much for the statements of Pytheas, who tells us, besides, that after he returned thence, he traversed the whole coasts of Europe from Gades to the Don."

Oddly, Strabo in an apparent attempt at fairness, commented elsewhere, "However, in regard to celestial phenomena and in mathematical speculation Pytheas appears to have treated the facts correctly . . . (as also in saying that) among those who dwell near the frigid zone there is either complete absence or very considerable shortage of cultivated crops and domestic animals and nourishment consists mainly of millet, wild fruits, herbs, grasses, and roots. Those who manage to raise cereals have also honey and the mead made from it. But not having enough clear weather, they convey the ripened grain into large buildings and thresh it there indoors, since otherwise the lack of sun and the abundance of rain would ruin the harvest."

The problem was, as so often with sheltered scholars who copy each other from generation to generation, what was beyond established knowledge and mental grasp could not be true.

Not until the mathematician, astronomer, and geographer Claudius Ptolemy of Alexandria again mapped the world in the second century A.D. did Pytheas regain credibility. Ptolemy accepted Pytheas' finding that Thule was the northernmost known land, located it at 63°, and Thule became common scholarly property until Elizabethan times. Ptolemy's map had Britain and Ireland about where Eratosthenes put them on Pytheas' information, but strangely showed nothing of the Baltic Sea and little of Scandinavia except an island of "Scandia" north of Germany.

Many oceanographers, geographers, historians, and classicists of the past two centuries have looked into the Pytheas story, some briefly, some in speculative detail. They too have had to build largely on Strabo's back-handed detail.

Among early nineteenth-century historians was M. D. A. Azuni, who in 1813 published *Mémoires pour servir à l'histoire des anciens navigateurs de Marseille* in Paris, quoting extensively from Strabo but celebrating

Pytheas as a hero of his city, one of the oldest in continuous existence.

Exhaustive studies have been made by Sir Edward H. Bunbury and Sir Clements R. Markham, distinguished Victorian geographers who credited Pytheas as "discoverer of Britain" in 1879 and 1893 respectively; by C. F. C. Hawkes, a professor at Oxford University, in the J. L. Myres memorial lecture at New College in 1975, with intricate theories on Pytheas' route; and by Rhys Carpenter, Bryn Mawr College classicist. Carpenter put more than fifty years into illumination of Greek exploration westward through the Mediterranean, from the dozen Phocaean cities of western Turkey where Ionian Greeks had migrated six hundred years before Christ, to be driven west again by Medes and Persians, on through centuries that put them in Sicily, Italy, France, and Spain.

Others fascinated by Pytheas include E. H. Warmington, reader in ancient history at the University of London, and his associate Max Carey; J. V. Luce, reader in classics at Trinity College, Dublin; and Vilhjálmur Stefánsson, the Arctic explorer.

Stefánsson, who knew his northern seas, was certain Pytheas described ground-up floating ice with his report of a cold, white, gelatinous mass, translated both as looking like marine sponges and, more popularly, as "sea lungs" or shoals of his Mediterranean jellyfish (*pulmo marinus*). This proved, Stefánsson contended vigorously, that Pytheas got almost to Iceland, his Thule. (George Reiger, a modern nature writer, suggested in a Yale University lecture that Thule might even have been Greenland.)

But Luce, echoing Markham's preference for Norway, called the white mass just "a chilling sea fog off the Norwegian coast." (Off Norway it would not have been ice, for the North Atlantic drift brings the warm water of our Gulf Stream close, and probably did then.)

Bunbury, noting that much of Pytheas' report had to be based on hearsay–as were many of Herodotus'–cautioned that "the extravagant pretensions that have been put forward by some modern writers on his behalf, contending that he carried his personal explorations as far as the Vistula on the one hand, and the Shetland Islands, or even Iceland, on the other, have tended to increase the air of fable thrown around his voyage, and have led some critics in very recent times to follow the example of Polybius and Strabo, and reject the whole story as a fiction."

Bunbury credited Pytheas with introducing the name Thule to ancient geography, doubted that he ever reached there, but praised him as "the first Greek writer who gave any account of the British Isles at all."

He credited Pytheas further with being "first to embody in his work a considerable amount of new information concerning the north-west of Europe. . . . That portion of the map of Europe, which in the time of Herodotus had been a mere blank, had now been partially filled up."

Nathaniel Bowditch himself may never have thought of it, but present editions of his *American Practical Navigator* give almost a page to Pytheas, with this reminder: "He was not the first to venture upon the sea, and even in his time man was the inheritor of his predecessors' knowledge." This might be kept in mind with hundreds of voyages of discovery. No matter what a man thought he was first to see, there was always the chance, often the probability, that somebody else had been there first but left no notarized record. There are historians – mandarin Samuel Eliot Morison was vehemently *not* among them – and non-Establishment archeologists and epigraphers who think Phoenicians may have seen American shores centuries before St. Brendan's monks, Madog the Welsh prince, or Leif Eiriksson's Vikings, or before Columbus, Vicente Yánez Pinzón, Hernando Cortés, Vasco Núnez Balboa, Juan Ponce de León, Ferdinand Magellan, the Cabots and Corte Reals (father and sons), or any of our modern "age of discovery."

There are even a few who feel that man has been sailing the seas so much longer than history knows that it is possible that the world was "encompass'd" once or more in an unremembered past before the voyages of Magellan, completed by Juan Sebastián Delcano, and Sir Francis Drake. Such a voyage, exploratory or following known trade routes, might have taken years, even one or more lifetimes and successive ships, but men who want to touch the horizon have always been with us. And men have been building ships for longer than we know. Herodotus tells of the three-year Phoenician circumnavigation, east to west, of Africa about 600 B.C. for Egypt's Pharoah Necho, two thousand years before Bartolomeu Dias and Vasco da Gama rounded Africa's "Cabo Tormentoso," west to east.

Accepting Pytheas' story, questions remain. One voyage or two? What kind of ship or ships? If one or more than one voyage, over how many months or years? (Markham guessed six years.) Was Iceland or Norway or Greenland his Thule? Did he sail around Britain, his Pritania, or walk over much of it, or both? Did he see Ireland, his Iernê, and its gold, or just hear about it? How did he get along with the Veneti of Armorica, our Brittany, those busy and rich middlemen in the cassiterite and elektron trades? How with the Abalans (the Danes) and the Balts of Samland (Prussia and Poland), who gathered elektron where it washed up–and still does–on Baltic beaches?

Possibly, though not certainly, the first question can be answered with, "one voyage." It is hard to suppose the Carthaginians would let him by the Pillars a second time. Yet Rhys Carpenter thinks he went by with their permission and sets the time at around 250 B.C., when Carthage was already fourteen years into its first Punic War with Rome. As recorded by Strabo and earlier by a more friendly historian, Diodorus Siculus, Pytheas gathered more on life and people in Britain than a fast-moving tourist might be expected to learn. Thus Markham's six-year estimate may be valid.

We may guess that if Pytheas made a later visit at least to Albion, southern England, he went from Massalia up the Rhône River and down the Loire, or from Narbonne up the Aude, through the Carcassonne Gap to the Garonne, the "Narbo-Burdigala Traverse," to be carried to the Atlantic. A Veneti leather ship would take him to Devon or Kent, but to keep a secret, probably not to Cornwall's tin mines. He would walk there, Diodorus, Strabo, and Pliny mentioning his report of a six-day journey inland to the mines.

Markham also assumed that Pytheas used a big warship, Massalia being famous for shipbuilding for its own navy and merchants and for Rome. But could he count on provisions for a big crew and soldiers to protect him? How maintain discipline so far from home? A guess at least may be made that a small ship, a "round ship" or gaulos such as developed by the Phoenicians for their extensive trade on and beyond the Mediterranean and adapted by the Greeks after them, would have been more practical, whether he was captain or passenger.

Iceland or Norway or Greenland? Norwegian historians think of Pytheas as their discoverer, but any discovery must have been on the way back from the northwest Atlantic, at least from the Shetlands, his Haemodae. Greenland is a possibility, but the distance is great, mostly against prevailing winds, with only a bleak, dangerous coast to be approached.

Circumnavigation of Britain might require still another ship but with the use of Keltoi, the *lingua franca* then, he could have chartered one with a crew familiar with the Irish Sea as well as the English Channel and North Sea.

Whether one voyage or two, could Pytheas have answered all questions for his own serious historians? Timaeus of Athens wanted living details. What were people of Armorica, Pritania, Abalus, Iernê like? What did they eat, drink, wear, look like? What did they make? What crops and animals did they raise? What kind of homes did they build? Strabo and Diodorus reported that Pytheas did tell much of this about the Pritani.

Possibly too many Greek intellectuals wanted to now only whether the "barbarians" with their tongues like the "twittering of birds" read meaning into stars. (Pytheas would have scorned astrology!) Still, he could gather information on native religions, Druid or whatever, as Diodorus reported, and tell of Greek gods who now were taken less seriously. Zeus' bolts probably frightened few.

Throughout he would see the northern heavens, with the three polar stars near the tip of the Little Bear's tail higher than at home by ten or more degrees to tell more emphatically their importance to navigators. (Our Polaris had not yet moved almost over the North Pole.) The great tides of Brittany and the Channel Islands might have hinted to him of gravitational interrelationships of all heavenly bodies.

He probably wondered why southern England, particularly Cornwall, had such a temperate climate so far above Massalia's latitude. Perhaps some Basque or Galician or Irish seafarer told him of that warm "river in the sea," the Gulf Stream. Certainly Ponce de León's navigating officer Alaminos in 1513 was only the first to *record* it. Five years later Peter Martyr was first to suggest it as part of a great wind-driven system, now called the North Atlantic gyre.

Not until Europe's Renaissance did more than a scattering of minds reach for answers Pytheas sought.

There were brilliant enough men of his time and after him: astronomers like his contemporary Herakleides of Pontus, Sicily, and later Hipparchus of Rhodes. There were the mathematician Euclid of Alexandria and the physicist Archimedes of Syracuse. There was the geographer Eratosthenes, who was to calculate the circumference of the world within two hundred miles.

But intellectual fashion went another way. Aristotle's Peripatetics, led by Dicaearchus, wanted only the late master's concepts. Serious thinkers had to look to Alexandria. Many Greeks, having strayed from astronomy to astrology, also argued endlessly about morals, and as futilely as we still do.

In history Alexander's generals, the Diadochi, inherited his empire after his death in Babylon in 323 B.C., then fought each other until 281. Carthage had spent much of the fourth century fighting Greece over Sicily. Rome and Carthage started the long Punic wars in 264. When they ended in 146 Carthage and all its culture were salted rubble. The same year saw Rome's final conquest of Greece, to rule the Mediterranean world. Ahead lay Julius Caesar's conquest of Gaul and Iberia—with destruction of any remnants of Tartessan civilization—and of Britain. *Pax Romana* meant obliteration of almost all not Roman.

Massalia maintained an even position until she finally became an ally of Rome. Her only misstep was letting Pompey enter the city, thus offending Caesar. He did not take destructive revenge, possibly because he needed Massalia-built ships to haul grain from North Africa for Rome's growing population.

But it appears, lacking records or "folk wisdom," that no one from Massalia or any Mediterranean port followed Pytheas. The oldest coin found in England is a Greek piece with Artemis embossed, possibly left by Pytheas. Caesar's legions midway in the first century B.C. were the next Mediterranean men known to set foot on Britain.

Massalia remembered Pytheas. It refused to let the scornful Polybius enter for information for his geography book. This ironically deprived us of much knowledge of Massalia. Today, Marseille may be looked at as Pytheas' monument, and honored for having produced him, with his Ionian faith that science is an art to control nature to better the human lot.

If in time Pytheas' *Peri tou Okeanou* or any fragment is found, like the Dead Sea Scrolls, hidden from bigots by some unknown ancient scholar in a cave or monastery or forgotten library cellar, we may fill these gaps. Until then this imagined account of how he might have gone, with whom and where, may serve and perhaps stir other imaginations in an age gone technological.

Hampton, Virginia
July 15, 1984

JOHN AND HARRIET FRYE

WHO... WHAT... WHEN... WHERE...

Abalus Jutland, northern Denmark.

Abyla Apes' Hill, Ceuta, Morocco (African Pillar of Herakles).

Adriaticoseno Adriatic Sea.

Aesymnète archon or chief magistrate of Massalia, presumably chief executive.

Alalia Corsica.

Albion England.

Alexander the Great 356–323, King of Macedon.

Aliones Galicians, Basques.

Amphora (-ae) ceramic jar for storing or transporting wine, olive oil, or other liquids.

Anas River Guadiana River between Portugal and Spain.

Anaximander 611–547, Greek mathematician, astronomer, philosopher, pupil of Thales at Miletus.

Aparctias west wind.

Apeliotes east wind.

Aphrodite Venus (planet); Greek goddess of love.

Apollo Greek god of light and science, son of Zeus.

Arar River, Keltika Saône River, France.

Archimedes of Syracuse 287–212, discoverer of law of specific gravity.

Archon a magistrate of a Greek colony city.

Ares Mars (planet); Greek god of war.

Arganthonios c. 670–c. 550, King of Tartessos, reigned c. 630–550.

Argestes mistral; cold northwesterly gale.

Aristotle 384–322, Greek philosopher, student of natural world.

Arktos Ursa Major (Great Bear, Big Dipper).

Armorica Brittany, France.

Artabria, Iberia Galicia, Cantábria, northern coast of Spain.

Artemesia, Iberia Denia, Spain.

Artemis Greek goddess, protector of sailors, sister of Apollo, daughter of Zeus.

Artemon spritsail.

Auroch now extinct cattle-like animal of northern Europe.

Baetis River Guadalquivir River, Spain.

Balearico Sea Mediterranean area of Balearic Islands.

Balts East Prussians, Poles.

Basileia East Prussia, Poland (see *Samland*).

Belerion southwestern England.

Boreas northeast wind.

Borysthenes River Dnieper River, Russia.

Calbron westernmost Brittany.

Cape Nerium Finisterre, Spain.

Cape of the Cynetes Punta de Sagres, Portugal.

Cassiterides Scilly Islands, Cornwall, England.

Cassiterite tin (now tin oxide in mineralogy).

Cimbri inhabitants of southern Denmark.

Corbilo, Keltika Nantes, France.

Cubit ancient unit of measure, about 18 inches or the length of a man's forearm.

Curmi fermented grain drink, like beer, of Pritania (Britain).

Cynesians inhabitants of southern Portugal.

Cyneticum Algarve, the southern end of Portugal.

Cynosura Ursa Minor (Little Bear, Little Dipper).

Daesius Greek name of month (May–June) in which Alexander died.

Diadochi Alexander's generals and successors.

Diodorus Siculus Greek historian, fl. 60–21.

Drachma (-ae) ancient Greek coin.

Dumnonii ancient tribe of Devon, southern England.

Durius River, Lusitania Douro River, Portugal.

Durotriges ancient tribe of Cornwall, southern England.

Egyptiaco Pelago southern Mediterranean.

Elektron Greek name for amber.

Elektrum gold-silver alloy used in Greek coinage.

Emporiae, Iberia Ampurias, Spain.

Eratosthenes 276–196, for 50 years head of the Library of Alexandria, first to measure earth's circumference.

Eridanus River Elbe River, Germany.

Erythraean Sea Indian Ocean.

Euclid of Alexandria mathematician, fl. 300 B.C., who developed geometry into a system still in use.

Euxine Sea Black Sea.

Gadeira Cádiz, Spain (Carthaginian name; Phoenician *Gadir*; Roman *Gades*).

Galatic Gulf Gulf of Lyons.

Gargoris god-founder of Tartessos.

Garumna River, Keltika Garonne River, France.

Gaul France (Roman).

Gaulos small Mediterranean trading ship of ancient times.

Gulf of Metuonis Baltic Sea.

Gulf of Oestrymnis Bay of Biscay.

Gutones inhabitants of Sweden.

Haemodae Shetland Islands.

Helios the sun.

Hellespont Dardanelles.

Herakleia, Iberia Carteya, Spain.

Herakleides of Pontus fourth century B.C. Greek astronomer

Hermes Mercury (planet); Greek god of swift communication.

Herodotus Greek historian, 484–424.

Hipparchus of Rhodes fl. 160–125, Greek mathematician, founder of trigonometry.

Hypanis River, Samland Bug River, Poland.

Hyperborea far northern lands from Mediterranean.

Iberia Spain and Portugal.

Ichnussa Sardinia.

Ictis, Belerion St. Michael's Mount, Cornwall.

Iernê Ireland.

Illipla, Tartessos Niebla, Andalucía, Spain.

Isocrates 426–338, Athenian orator and teacher, pupil of Socrates.

Ister River Danube River.

Kalpé Gibraltar, European Pillar of Herakles.

Kantion Kent, England.

Keltika Celtic France.

Keltoi Celts, Celtic.

Kolaeus sixth century B.C. Greek mariner and trader from Samos.

Kromyoussa Mallorca (Balearics).

Kronos Saturn (planet); Greek god of time.

Libs southwest wind.

Libya North Africa from Egypt west to the Atlantic Ocean; inhabited by Maurusians.

Liger River, Keltika Loire River, France.

Lusitania Portugal.

Luxium River, Iberia Odiel River, Andalucía, Spain.

Mainaké, Iberia Málaga, Spain.

Massalia Marseille, France.

Maurusians inhabitants of Libya.

Meloussa Minorca (Balearics).

Meton Athenian astronomer (fl. 421 B.C.), discoverer of moon's 19-year cycle.

Mictis Isle of Wight, England (also called *Vectis*).

Mycenae Agamemnon's capital in Argolis, 1600–1500.

Narbo, Keltika Narbonne, France.

Notus south wind.

Obol small Greek coin, circulated in Massalia.

Oestrymnides Channel Islands.

Oestrymnis, Iberia northwestern Spain.

Okeanos Atlantic Ocean.

Olispo, Lusitania Lisboa, Portugal.

Olympiad Greek four-year period, between Olympic games.

Onuba, Tartessos Huelva, Spain.

Orcades Orkney Islands.

Orcas Unst, Shetland Islands.

Pentekonter large ancient Greek warship.

Periplus ancient coastal pilot book.

Philolaos of Croton Greek astronomer, b. c. 480 B.C., first to propound doctrine of motion of the earth.

Pityoussa Ibiza (Balearics).

Plato Greek philosopher, 429–347.

Polybius 205–122, Greek historian and geographer.

Pontus Pelagus Mediterranean Sea (Homer).

Pou Kernou Cornwall, England.

Pritania Britain.

Promontorium Ophiussae Cabo Roca, Portugal.

Promontorium Sacrum Cabo São Vicente, Portugal.

Ptolemy Soter Alexander's governing satrap at Alexandria, founder of Library of Alexandria.

Rhodai, Iberia Rosas, Spain.

Rhodanus River, Keltika Rhône River, France.

Samâra River, Keltika Somme River, France.

Samland Prussia and Poland.

Sardoö Pelago Western Mediterranean.

Sea lungs jellyfish (*pulmo marinus*).

Selene the moon.

Sequana River, Keltika Seine River, France.

Stadium Greek linear measurement, 606 feet 9 inches (length of sports stadium).

Staters ancient gold coin originated by Philip II of Macedon.

Stonehenge ancient stone monument in southern England.

Strabo 64 B.C.–A.D. 21, Greek geographer.

Tamesis River Thames River, England.

Tanaïs River mythical European river thought to flow both north and south between Baltic and Black Seas.

Tartessos ancient kingdom, now Andalucía, Spain.

Tartessos River Guadalquivir River, Spain.

Teutoni Germans.

Thales of Miletus 640–546, Greek mathematician, founder of geometry.

Thanet northeastern tip of Kent, England.

Tharsis Tartessan capital, now Sevilla, Spain.

Thule probably Iceland, possibly Greenland or Norway.

Timaeus of Athens c. 345–250, Greek historian.

Timuques the 600 governing oligarchs of Massalia.

Tyrenno Tyrrhenian Sea.

Uexisamé, Uxisama Ushant, Île d'Ouessant.

Urium River, Iberia Río Tinto, Andalucía, Spain.

Vectis Isle of Wight, England (also called *Mictis*).

Veneti Bretons.

Viadua River, Samland Oder River, Germany.

Zephyrus the west wind.

Zeus Jupiter (planet).

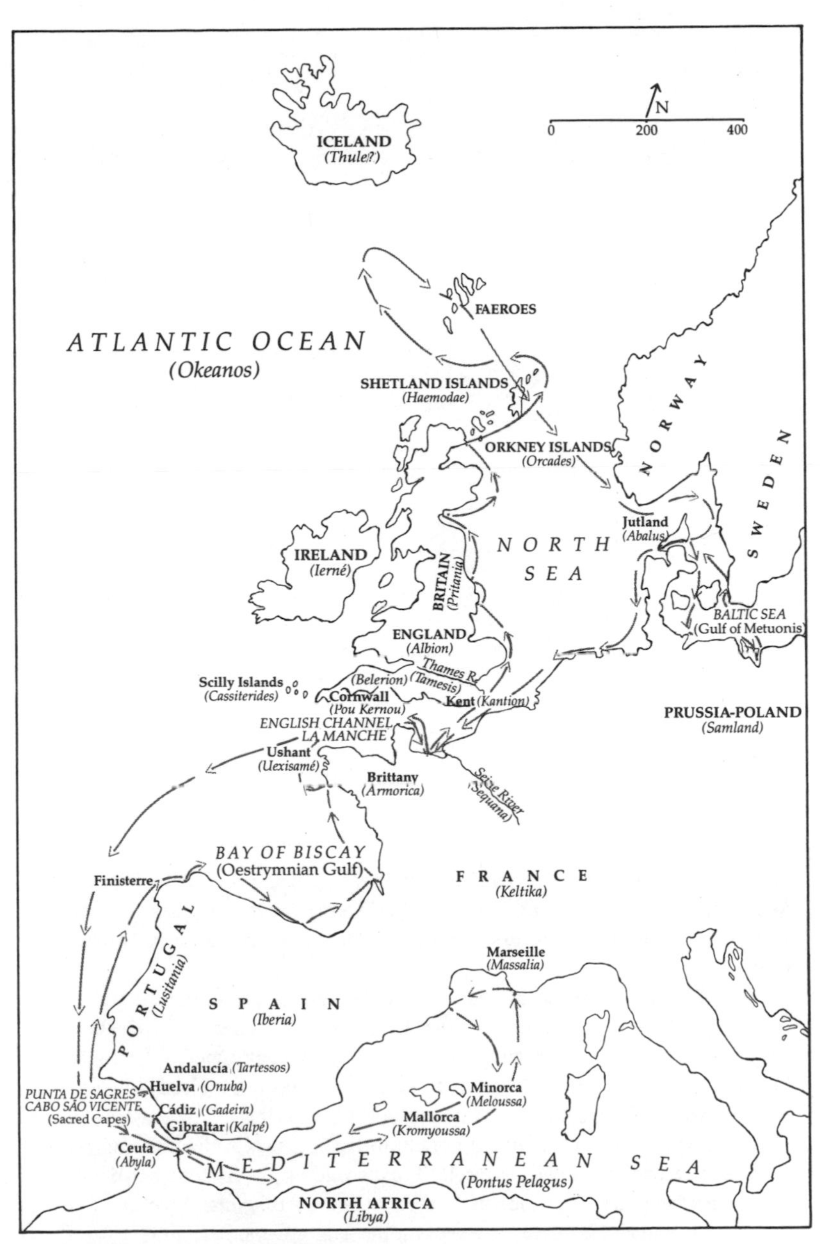

Probable Route of Pytheas' Voyage

Overleaf:

These are shores believed visited by Pytheas, to bring the first definitive knowledge of northern Europe back to the Mediterranean Sea, later to give Eratosthenes, head of the Library of Alexandria, information for his world map.

Latitudes, or "climates," as measured by daylight hours on the summer solstice, the longest day, were recorded by Pytheas. Sir Clements Markham in 1893 fixed these places as having been visited by Pytheas: Oporto, Portugal, 15 hours; Ouessant (Ushant), Brittany, 16 hours; Flamborough Head, England, 17 hours; Tarbett Ness, Scotland, 18 hours; and Orcas (Unst), Shetlands, 19 hours.

Since natives then probably did not count by hours, Markham thought Pytheas measured these days himself. This would imply visits on solstice of five successive years, questionable in view of the Carthaginian blockade of the Strait of Gibraltar. However, as a geographer and astronomer, with mathematics necessarily mastered, Pytheas could have calculated the hours from his frequent angle sights with his gnomon or cross-staff by counting days ahead or back to solstice.

I

BACK OF THE NORTH WIND

THIS IS THE MOMENT I CAME FOR. No other the rest of my life can match it.

I am Pytheas of Massalia, astronomer and geographer from the blue sea far to the south, Homer's Pontus Pelagus, Our Sea in the middle of our world. We think we have come in our fat little gaulos farther north and west on Okeanos than anyone from Our Sea before us. Yet people may live farther, on some island or land I name Thule, the Farthest. The king at that northernmost island in the Haemodae told us that six or seven days' sail northwest there was a land of fire where nobody lived. Yet he had never been there, nor any of his people, and I had to know.

We now have been sailing or rowing for eight days, with squalls and calms and mists to confuse distance. I see birds to tell us Thule, if it is Thule, cannot be much farther.

We cannot reach it. Our gaulos, for all its stout sides and bottom, was built for nothing like this. It is surrounded by a cold, white jelly-like sea, looking almost like ours when we run into a shoal of sea lungs. The

---

Pytheas' small Mediterranean ship is in or near the Arctic Ocean, east or southeast of Iceland, his Thule. It has sailed the far northern reaches of Okeanos (the Atlantic) from the Haemodae (the Shetland Islands) into floating ice looking like the jellyfish Pytheas calls sea lungs. Aboard are a Tartessan captain and crew from the Urium River region of Iberia (the Río Tinto of southwestern Spain) and a Pritani (British) pilot. Their adventures have included a fight with Maurusian pirates from Libya, northern Africa. Waters beyond Iberia's Sacred Capes, the Cape of the Cynetes (Punta de Sagres) and Promontorium Sacrum (Cabo São Vicente), were known to Mediterranean men only by hearsay. Armorica (Brittany) they knew from overland trade in amber and tin.

Pytheas gives his ship's dimensions in cubits, a unit of about eighteen inches or the length of a man's forearm, and distances in stadia, a stadium equalling the length of a Greek athletic stadium, 606 feet nine inches or about one-tenth of a nautical mile.

The gaulos amid the "sea lungs," which scholars believe was pack ice, near Thule.

air is thick with a cold cloud lying on the sea. We cannot see where air and water meet. This fog makes it so much colder here, even only these few days past summer solstice, the longest day so many hours longer here, even endless.

We drift in near silence. There is no wind. We hear only the limp square sail slatting against the mast and the oaken hull and spars creaking in the low swell. The white stuff is too soft to walk on, but the men cannot put their oars into it easily because of scattered crystal-like chunks. Rowing farther would be brutal.

My captain, the Tartessan I call Jason after the leader of our Argonauts because I could not speak his name well at first, is uneasy. He has brought us this far to let me count the hours of the summer day back of the north wind, where Homer told us shepherd going out met shepherd coming home. Jason has kept his bargain and more, and so have the men, the eleven who survived with him when the Maurusian pirate drove their ship ashore near Massalia more than a year ago. We also have aboard his wise grandfather Girondas, who came to us at the well on the Urium River in Iberia, and Ogg, our Pritani pilot. But the Tartessans look at the white stuff and think of sunshine over blue waters.

Jason asked me to turn back. I stared ahead, hoping a rift would let me see more. We barely could see the thirty-cubit length of our gaulos. Even its fifteen-cubit beam seemed to shrink. We were wrapped in wool, in damp, cold wool that might be here forever, we with it.

"Yes, Jason, head back," I said at last. "We know what we have seen.

Nobody will believe us, but we know. My Thule will be there for another man."

Jason called and the men cheered. They forced their oars into the white stuff and swung the ship carefully, laboriously. Then they rowed slowly to keep from breaking oars. Now, exhausted from excitement, I could sleep.

In my last moments awake, I saw our straight track through the white stuff. Again I marveled at Jason and his helmsman Typhis. We cut across the swells at the supplement of the angle of our progress north and west. Jason applied geometry at sea as well as I on papyrus. While I slept, we reached open water.

We never saw sunrise but knew the day had to be about the same as at the Haemodae at solstice; there might have been neither sunrise nor sunset because we were still farther north. Later in the day, I asked Jason how far he thought we had gone from the Haemodae.

"Maybe five thousand stadia," he replied. "Hard to tell without knowing how fast we went over the bottom."

Five thousand stadia! How I wished for an island where we turned, and for sun. I could have gone ashore, set up my gnomon, and counted days back to solstice to find out how far we were north of the east-west line through Massalia, in degrees anyway. I had done this several times, lately with Eban, the Tartessan boy-sailor so anxious to learn our Greek science, since rounding westernmost Iberia, the Cape of the Cynetes and its twin, Promontorium Sacrum. I had also tried measuring the angle of the sun at sea with the mast for a gnomon and circles marked on deck to show distance from its base, but our gaulos was never steady enough. And I had used my cross-staff to sight the noon sun and the horizon at the same time, then measure the angle. This too needed firm footing.

Jason had showed me his own device—his hand on edge. He looked along two angled fingers at a star and the prow of the boat. He knew how high that star should be in Our Sea, and the difference told him about what my gnomon told me. Often he also held his fingers straight, sighted along the little finger at the horizon, and counted one, two, or three fingers above pointing to a star he knew.

Before falling asleep, I heard the men singing. I still knew only basics in Tartessan and asked Jason what the songs were about. The men had sung before, but these sounded different.

"Home," he said.

"I hear something about Alexandria and Syracuse and Piraeus, or do I?"

"You do. The girls at the quays." He sang with them softly.

On the foredeck Girondas led, singing a few words alone, the men joining in a chorus, all timed to the strokes of their oars.

"They saw girls at Armorica and other places, even at the Haemodae," I laughed.

"Not the same," Jason sighed. "Not the same."

II

HOW IT STARTED

HOW DID IT COME that I fell asleep shivering in this dank cloud with Jason and his Tartessans on a Massaliot gaulos?

Only last fall was the voyage thought of. Leaning over the stern and gazing toward Thule, I recalled our last devotions at the temples of Artemis and Apollo, Massalia's sister and brother gods, and our departure, a week after spring equinox. My wife Anticlea wept on the quay. Our son Dryas and daughter Anthia did not know whether to cry with her or cheer with the people. The Aesymnète, our archon or chief magistrate, many Timuques, our governing elders, and hundreds of citizens waved goodbye, or farewell.

There was a brief stop at Rhodai, our fight with the Maurusian pirates in the Balearico Sea, the night passage through the Pillars of Herakles, then Gadeira. There Jason and wine persuaded a Carthaginian officer that we had served him well.

There was the thrill after we rounded the two sacred capes and headed north on Okeanos. There was our first storm, frightening to me, no worry to Jason and his Tartessans. There were doubtful times among the suspicious Veneti of Armorica, who called my gnomon evil magic,

---

Pytheas describes the origins of the voyage and refers to places and peoples distant from his homeland. Among the places he mentions are Rhodai (Rosas) and Gadeira (Cádiz) in Iberia (Spain); Uexisamé (Ushant or L'Île d'Ouessant); Kantion (Kent, England); and Iernê (Ireland). He also speaks of the Erythraean Sea (the Indian Ocean) and of the Tanaïs, a mythical river that probably incorporated the north-flowing Vistula River of Poland and the south-flowing Dnieper of Russia. The Eridanus River (the Elbe), flowing into the North Sea, may also have been the northern Tanaïs. On its southeastern end, the Tanaïs supposedly issued into Lake Maeotis (the Sea of Azov) and the Euxine (the Black Sea).

Pytheas mentions too the Veneti of Armorica (Brittany) and the Keltoi (Celts) of Keltika, today's France and much of western Europe; also, the Gutones of what is now Sweden and the Teutoni and Balts who inhabited the region of northern Germany and Poland.

sail them. Do we have the man to lead the good men and bring them safely home, with, may we hope, knowledge to end our problem and increase our wealth, our well-being, and as important to us, our understanding of the world?"

Here he nominated me. He must have known of my latitude calculation fixing Massalia's spot on the Earth, its climate or zone, and my discovery of three almost unmoving stars so close above the Earth's axis.

Herakleides of Pontos discovered at least a generation ago that Earth spins on this axis through these stars. We also know of the five wandering stars, Hermes, Aphrodite, Ares, Zeus, and Kronos, that revolve around Helios the sun. Herakleides and some others suspect Earth is a sixth. We also know of the nearly nineteen-year cycle of Selene the moon.

The Timuques' vote was divided. There were some whose wealth depended on things as they were, others doubting that any man—especially a scientist who was no navigator—could expand their world. I probably would have been amused by the debate, especially at praise from men who understood little but had heard of my experiments with the sun's shadow from a gnomon, who knew I watched stars, and who liked, from the haven of middle life, anyone young, healthy, and enthusiastic.

Anyway, the Aesymnète prevailed, a decree was drafted, and the messenger was sent for me.

Even I knew that in politics all is not in open forum. Meton the vintner and Pasias the shipbuilder left the Timuques' hall for a sunny corner of the winery, where wine could be sipped amid quiet talk. I reconstruct their conversation here from what both told me later.

"Well, that's the best business the chief has done for a long time," said Meton. "The barbarians cut our profits thin. Do you have a ship Pytheas can use?"

"We're finishing a pentekonter," Pasias replied. "Warship big enough for anything. Launch in about a month."

"I know that one. Too big. Must be a hundred cubits. Look at all those rowers to feed."

"Yes, though it's the one that captain from Gadeira has his eye on. Thinks he could make it do better than a round ship for hauling. Fast trips, quick turnaround. You remember, the young fellow whose ship was driven ashore by those Maurusian pirates last summer. I can't say his name, though he's been around the yard with his crew of eleven men long enough. They're working to pay off their fines."

"What were they fined for?" Meton asked.

"You know—dancing in the streets. They were so happy when they were rescued, even though they lost everything. They started dancing and singing their old Tartessan songs at the quay. Against our law, and probably subversive songs at that."

"Yes, anything we can't understand must be subversive, or so we think," Meton said.

"And they couldn't pay, so I gave them work. They're good. The captain wants to keep them together until he can get another ship."

"Tartessans, not Carthaginians?"

"The captain is the only one who seems even to speak Carthaginian."

"Tartessans are the best sailors in the world," Meton mused. "Let's talk with him. He and Pytheas can work together. Let's tell him he can have a big ship later if he will take a little gaulos and bring Pytheas back full of what we want to know."

"Ah, but Meton, who's going to pay for this? It'll take him the rest of his life on my wages. And Pytheas himself is a poor man. He thinks money is only for books and trips to Athens to see Aristotle. Why, when he heard Alexander's satrap Ptolemy might start a library and academy at Alexandria, he borrowed money to go see. One of my ships took him. He didn't know if Ptolemy had asked Alexander about it, or even if he could get to see the man. Pytheas may be all fired up about stars and mathematics and science, but that's no wool on his children's backs in winter." (Pasias must know my neighbors!)

Meton looked at the sun through his wine and smiled.

"I think the chief will open the city treasury a little. He's put his prestige on this. He's not going to see it stopped for a few drachmae. Might squeeze a tiny obol or two out of his own pouch."

"What about stores?" Pasias asked. "Even a small ship has to feed its men."

"Oh, I'll see that it's stocked. Wine and olives and oil and grain. You take care of any extra gear from your chandlery. We'll get somebody to give samples of our bronze work to show the barbarians what we do with what they sell us. And when the gaulos comes back, the city can reward the Tartessan with any ship he wants and forget the fine."

This put their minds back to trade and the political world of our city with its crowded harbor, busy streets, citadel and temples of Artemis and Apollo on the hill, and walls, with farms and vineyards beyond. All now was at peace, Greek, in our own world, far from Sparta, farther from Athens, asking favors of nobody, Greek, Roman, or Carthaginian. Still, far off in Asia was Alexander, as Meton said, "conquering and conquering and conquering." A Macedonian but thinking himself a Greek, loving Athens as much as Athens despised him.

Meton tipped his cup to the sun. "Where's he going next, Pasias? A conqueror has to go on conquering. He can't stop. He'll make a grand tour of the world–India . . . Etruria . . . Rome . . . Carthage . . . Who knows even where he is now? We have had no word for months."

"Oh, why worry?"

"You'll see. Alexander will look at us as a friendly little stepping stone, to be stepped on if we don't mind, to be kicked out of the way if we do. Then Keltika and Iberia and whatever is beyond."

Pasias shook his head. "You make it dismal enough, Meton. Drink your wine. It's your best in years. Wine's for washing away such thoughts."

"Amen to that, Pasias, but I'm for finding out all we can about the west and north. We may have to know. Let's get Pytheas and the Tartessans off to sea."

III

THE TARTESSANS

THE MESSENGER led me to the Hall of the Timuques. I had been there often, but to our Library, never to a high office.

As we came to the Aesymnête's rooms, I saw Meton and Pasias come out. The vintner and the shipbuilder always had business there. The Aesymnête received me at once. He repeated what he had told the Timuques and said my mission was not to conquer or colonize, but to "sail to the ends of our Earth to find out what we need to know." Meton and Pasias would help, he added.

I promised my best. I left to tell my family, then to find ships and men – me, a scientist!

On the marble steps the two middle-aged men introduced themselves.

"Yes," I said, surprised. "I was going to see you."

We walked in the fall sun back to Meton's winery, to be served with his best. They told me of the Tartessans and how they might fit into this venture.

"Our law against dancing in the streets is foolish and I was foolish to vote for it," Meton said. "I feel like dancing myself when we get a good grape harvest and the wine is golden. But this time there may be profit in the law. There are plenty of Massaliot captains and sailors who could do well, but nobody is better at sea than a Tartessan. Tartessos ruled the seas outside the Pillars of Herakles when Phoenicia's Biblos, Tyre, and Sidon were fishing villages."

I promised to talk to the Tartessans.

Pytheas hears about the little ship he will be given, a gaulos or "round ship" based on an ancient Phoenician type. It is the sort of vessel used by merchants for voyages to Mainaké (Málaga), last port east of the Pillars of Herakles, and to Sicily. His shipbuilder also trades through the Hellespont (Dardanelles) to the Euxine.

"Their captain will work with you, I am sure," Pasias said. "All he wants now is to get to sea again."

"What about a ship?" I asked. "I am no sailor. I know nothing about ships except as a passenger – too often a sick one!"

"Pytheas, that will be easy. We have a little gaulos which should be about right. It's only two years old and one of the best my men have built. We use it trading to Mainaké and Syracuse. It has a big cargo hold but it can be handled by a dozen good men. It's tubby and slow, but in calm seas it can be rowed forty stadia or better an hour. It sails as fast downwind and I'll bet these Tartessans can sail into a headwind. They'll trim that sail so flat you'll gain maybe a stadium forward for eight or ten across the wind."

"I don't follow your geometry," I laughed, "but I don't know ships."

"Come to the yard tomorrow and see the little ship," Pasias said. "And the Tartessans. They're a happy bunch."

We parted, pleased with each other, whether from the fine wine or from prospects of the voyage. Things seemed to be ordering themselves, perhaps too fast. These businessmen made all sound simple, but they would not be with me and the Tartessans.

My first thought had been to try to start by earliest spring, perhaps before equinox. Equinox would bring the last gales of winter, but more day than night. I knew that the farther north I went, the longer would be those days from equinox to solstice.

I felt that although most of our masters called Earth the center of the universe, the sun might be, with Earth and the five wandering stars moving around it. My voyage might tell us.

I was excited. My Anticlea was alarmed. Dryas wanted to go along, with all his ten years. Little Anthia asked for a playtoy from another land.

The next day I went to Pasias' shipyard and wondered if I dared go ahead. There was a big ship on the ways, looking almost ready to launch. Many oarports. A pentekonter, an old man watching from the shade of a tree told me. "Beautiful, beautiful," he said. "Pasias' men are masters." It all looked mysterious, even though I knew Massalia had built ships during all our three centuries, and for all nations on Our Sea.

Most of the shipwrights looked like everyday Massaliots. Among them were a dozen ragged men, their skins sun-dark. Only one had no thick black beard. "Those must be the Tartessans," I thought. "They look more like pirates than victims."

Pasias beckoned. "You come early," he said. "Good. We will show you around and talk to the Tartessans. I have told them nothing, though tavern gossip likely told them plenty last night. My men know more about what's going on than I do."

"Gossip is just as fast at the Academy," I said. "But, is that the ship? It looks tremendous."

"No," he replied. "Your gaulos could be hoisted on its deck with a half dozen more. I'll show you yours. First, let's talk to the Tartessan captain." He called a name that sounded like "Jaxon" or "Yasson." One bearded man left his work, the others watching but not stopping.

He was a short, wiry man who walked lightly and surely through yard litter. I felt that he could leap from mountain rock to rock with any goat. He looked about my age, seven or eight Olympiads. Pasias talked to him in mixed Greek and Carthaginian. Then he introduced us. The man smiled and said in broken Greek, "You read stars."

"Yes," I said. "Do you?" I knew Tartessos once had a civilization like our own, perhaps a written language and mathematics, all now lost.

"Stars tell me where I am at sea," he replied.

Pasias told him our proposal. The man asked to see the gaulos. We went to the quay where about ten ships, small and large, were moored. Pasias had a large fleet, as well as his yard. He traded widely about Our Sea, across the Egyptiaco Pelago to the new city of Alexandria, to the Tyrreno and Adriaticoseno, and even to the Euxine, far to the east through the Hellespont.

We went aboard a small boat. It looked trim and solid, but could this do what we were to do? The Tartessan went over it plank by plank, rib by rib, spar by spar. He often stuck his knife into the wood, once deeply.

"We will replace that plank," Pasias said, "and any others."

We found the hold dry. The man looked carefully where the mast butt rested in a small, stout cradle on the heavy timber backbone, also at the timbers rising from the backbone farthest forward and back. He crawled and reached into the smallest places.

After an hour, and many questions, the Tartessan said, "I will talk to my men."

Pasias called the Tartessans to his overseer's shelter. The Massaliot shipwrights watched curiously.

The captain spoke to his men in that lyrical language that neither Pasias nor I understood. He pointed to the pentekonter, then to the gaulos. Several men asked questions which got ready answers, or the captain asked Pasias. These were free men, not Carthaginian slaves, here at least. I had supposed that Carthage had enslaved all Tartessans, as well as those they had driven into the copper and silver mines, often to die of exhaustion.

Cautious smiles slowly replaced doubtful frowns under the heavy beards. The men moved away and talked among themselves. They seemed to take a vote. The captain came back.

"We will do it," he said.

IV

GETTING READY

WINTER PASSED QUICKLY. Things happened too fast at times. My mind already was crowded. Pasias, Meton, and many others of Massalia's merchants and traders kept promises. A few did refuse to help, but when winter began to turn to spring, much was in order. Food, including wheat, barley, millet, dried fish, and cheese, amphorae and skins of wine and olive oil, and other stores were ready to go aboard. I was given a copy of our old periplus to help us at least to Gadeira, although the Tartessans knew the way well. I had my own maps of the shores of Our Sea, drawn from my travels and from talking with captains.

The gaulos was hauled out. The Tartessans climbed all over it. The pentekonter had been work; the gaulos was liberation. They replaced the half-rotted plank and a few others. They forced papyrus tow into seams, then covered them with hot pitch. They refastened the lead sheathing over pitched wool on the bottom.

The captain spent several hours one sunny day squatting on the ground up the ways. He stared at the gaulos' hull, at the smooth, rounded bottom and the big timber running the full length along the middle. With a stick he scratched in the dirt. After he had made and covered over many marks, he drew one that satisfied him. I saw that he had drawn the cross-section curve of the bottom at its widest and put a vertical projection underneath. It was a neat drawing, such as a mathematician's for a geometry problem.

Pytheas learns of Abalus (Jutland), a source of much amber, and of the old Tartessan city of Onuba (Huelva) located at the junction of the Luxium (Odiel) and the Urium rivers. Mentioned too is Illipla, the ruined fortress at what is now Niebla, up the Urium near the great copper and silver mines of Andalucía.

The captain showed Pasias the drawing. He asked for two big planks, each a cubit or more wide.

"You can have the planks," Pasias said, "but what will this do for the ship? We keep the bottoms clear so the ships can be hauled on beaches in storms."

"You will see," the captain replied. "It will sail better. When the wind is from the side, we will keep a better course. We will not slide, as these gaulos always do."

"If so," Pasias said, "you have made every ship I build from now on better. But how does it work?"

The captain took a small piece of soft wood and whittled a rough model of a hull. He put it in water. "Push it sideways," he told Pasias. Pasias leaned and pushed with his fingers. The model moved easily.

The captain then fitted a thin flat piece of wood to the bottom vertically and put it back in the water. He had to fasten a pebble on the lower edge.

"Now push," he said. Pasias pushed again and smiled.

"Pick your planks and do it."

In a few days the Tartessans had pulled two well-seasoned planks from Pasias' stock and hewed and shaped them to what looked to me much like the lines of a slender fish. The upper plank was almost as long as the hull bottom itself, the lower perhaps half. The men smoothed them with rough stones. They pitched the matching edges and pinned them together with heavy wooden pegs driven into holes they had bored and burned.

They then used long timbers for levers, raised the hull high, and blocked it solidly. They coated the bottom of the hull's center timber and the top edge of the new piece with pitch. Again using stout pegs, they pinned the whole to the bottom timber, covered it with wool and sheet lead, put a heavy lead shoe on the lower edge, and then shaped two bronze straps to follow the sides of the hull and hook over the side rail.

Pasias called his own foremen to watch. "Remember what you see," he told them. "If it helps, we will do it too." He turned to the captain. "Where did you get this idea?"

"My grandfather told me what his grandfather told him," the captain said. "When Tartessos was free, we built great ships."

"Do you build them this way for the Carthaginians at Gadeira?" Pasias asked. "I never noticed their ships sailing any better than ours."

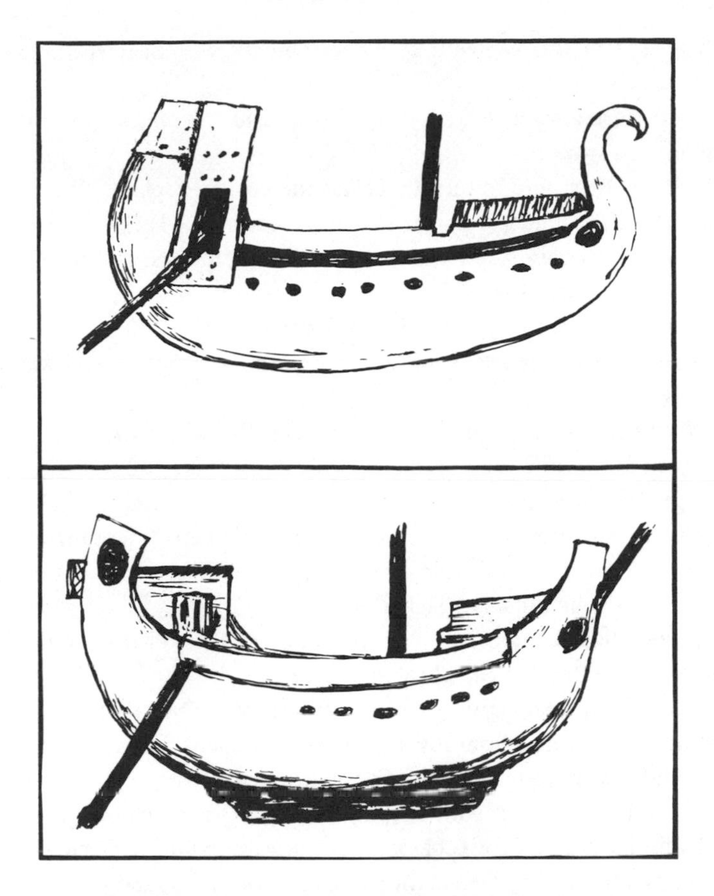

A Phoenician gaulos, above, and Jason's modification, with keel, below. Without the keel a gaulos was easy to beach, but the keel made it possible to sail closer to the wind and to hold course.

"Let them build their own pots."

The captain and Pasias went into a technical discussion. I missed much but saw that the captain was going to teach me more geometry and physics. I knew them from books, he from practice. He was explaining how the wind affected a boat and a sail from different angles, and how it could be made to help move a boat forward from almost any quarter but dead ahead.

The captain also wanted bigger steering oars, with heavier shafts and wide blades.

"Ours have always steered well," Pasias said. "Won't bigger ones be too hard to swing?"

"We want the ship to turn quickly," the captain replied. "We have a man who can swing it if our helmsman needs help." He pointed to one man who must have stood four and a half cubits tall and looked as wide, with great muscles free of fat.

"Make what you need," he told the captain.

Later the captain asked for heavier cloth to make a small sail for storms.

"We try not to get caught out," Pasias said. "When we see one coming, we make for a harbor or a beach. If we can't get there, we take in all sail and either drift or try to row. And we don't sail in winter at all."

"Where you want us to go," the captain explained, "there may be no harbors. A small sail will steady the ship in a gale. We do this all the time out beyond your Pillars of Herakles."

He soon had cut and sewn a small triangular sail. What it would do I could not see, but the captain was content.

I got to know him better. I visited evenings when the Tartessans were resting from labor, I from my studies of all I could find about the seas and lands we were to explore. The men lived aboard, even while the gaulos was on the ways, with sleeping pallets on the hold floor. The ship had a firepot on deck for cooking. They always invited me below and I found it snug and dry, even in the worst rains of winter, and warmer than outside when the northwest argestes chilled the coast.

I never did get the captain's name just right and asked to call him Jason, for our Greek hero of a great voyage many centuries ago. The huge man, his boatswain, I called Herakles. Herakles was another Argonaut, I told Jason. I named our helmsman after the Argonauts' Typhis.

As we learned each other's language, Jason told me of his life and that of the few pure Tartessans left along the Iberian coast after two centuries of enslavement. Massalia knew only the broad story of how Carthage had established herself at Phoenician Gadir, renamed it Gadeira, and even pushed us out of some of our trade settlements between here and the Pillars.

Jason's whole life as a man has been at sea. He is the son and grandson and beyond of sailors. His grandfather sailed, an unwilling captain for the Carthaginians, to some lands we are to seek and came back with elektron, purchased from the Veneti of Armorica. The Veneti had brought it in their leather-covered boats from still farther north, from a land called Abalus, where it washed out on beaches. They also brought the mottled white knucklebone ingots of cassiterite from the Cassiterides, the land or islands to the west. The Veneti too must be great sailors, but not so far-ranging as the ancient Tartessans.

Jason's grandfather and a few other Tartessans still live in a ruined Tartessan fortress called Illipla, up the copper-colored Urium River that flows into Okeanos northwest of Gadeira. The river waters cannot be drunk, Jason says, because they are poisoned by copper in the mines around Illipla. Birds and animals seek pools of rainwater.

I asked Jason once if he really were pure Tartessan. He smiled. "Almost. When we were still free, one of your Greek sailors fell in love with a Tartessan woman at Onuba. That was long ago. They were two of my ancestors."

"What was his name?" I asked.

"Simonides. Simonides of Samos."

"Was he a sailor for Kolaeus?"

"Yes, Kolaeus, I was trying to remember. Kolaeus came to our harbor where the Urium and the Luxium meet at Onuba, in a storm. He had trading goods he said he was taking to Egypt. He sold them to the Tartessans for silver. Tartessos had much silver and did not know how or why other people valued it so. He took away many bars. He used some for anchors and left us his stone and lead anchors. He sailed back to Samos. We never saw him again. But Simonides stayed. Some say he was my grandfather's grandfather, others think he was that grandfather's grandfather. It was long ago."

He added that no Tartessan had willingly married a Carthaginian. The Carthaginians considered the people of Tartessos almost animals – a humiliation that enabled them to save for generations the story of their glory. The Carthaginians neither knew nor cared what they were talking about.

"We have songs the Carthaginians would kill us for," Jason said. "We make great fun of them and they never know it."

"Do you hope to get your freedom again, Jason?" I asked.

"It is too late. Some Tartessans still live free far inland, but we are too few and too scattered. They let me and my men have a ship because we make voyages they don't dare to try. But they take the profits. When they see us again, they may try to make us pay for the ship the pirates wrecked. I will have to think of something to tell them. You think, too. We must get past Gadeira, but we must stop there too or we will be in real trouble."

"I do know two mathematicians there," I said. "We met at Alexandria once. They seemed like nice fellows and told me I ought to go to Carthage and see their big library. I think their mathematics was for money-lending."

"Money is all they think of. They think they take it with them when they die."

"So do a lot of us," I laughed.

Our gaulos, freshly painted and its oculi at the prow brightened, was ready a week before equinox. Jason, Pasias, and the crew took it for a day-long trial sail. I went along to see what I was getting into. We returned with Pasias enthusiastic about what Jason had done to the hull.

The men loaded our stores. Herakles carried two heavy amphorae of wine or oil at a time, the others one apiece. Jason watched constantly from the quay the way the gaulos sat in the water. He ordered each article stowed so that weight balanced weight, yet could be reached when needed. Slowly the ship eased lower in the water. When all was aboard and we all stood on deck, the gaulos seemed smaller. My own belongings were simple and light – clothes, writing materials, and most important, my gnomon, cross-staff, and hourglass, as well as a small water-clock I had devised, all for astronomical observations. These I wrapped in sheepskin and stowed where Jason promised they would stay dry.

I wondered where we would sleep and eat and how the men could row and handle sails, but Jason had this all worked out. At the benches there was still room for men to swing oars. All was clear where they would tend sail, handle mooring lines, or cook and eat. The men would sleep on deck in warm weather, huddle below in cold.

It was not luxury, Meton and even Pasias would scorn it. It was the life of a sailor and I would live it. I wanted nothing better than these men had.

After loading, equinoctial gales kept us at the quay day after day. Even the sun seemed to have forsaken our shores. I was impatient, but Pasias laughed. "I have seen ships lost for somebody being impatient."

"But," I protested, "we have less than three months before solstice and we do not know how far we are going."

"You'll go soon enough. Just remember, we will all be safe in dry beds when you are on the open sea, wondering what in the world you are doing out there."

The gales ended and spring came upon the land and sea. The day was set. It was a holiday to be remembered. Criers roamed the streets. We all walked to the temples of Artemis and Apollo. We needed their blessings, Artemis as our goddess of the sea and seamen, Apollo for his love of what was Back of the North Wind. These gods and all Olympus must have marveled at the turnout . . . the Aesymnète, the Timuques with Meton and Pasias standing alongside him, citizens including townsmen and tillers from beyond the walls, women and children. Jason and his Tartessans joined in, having already fastened a small carving of their Sun God to the gaulos' mast.

From the temples we all walked to Pasias' quay. Everybody was festive but my Anticlea. She clung to me, wishing, I knew, only that the voyage were ending, not starting.

We were all aboard. Jason gave the order to cast off. The men pushed the gaulos from the quay and a light breeze from the hills helped her away. The sail was freed from the yardarm smartly. I watched with wonder at the easy skill of the men.

Jason gave the lee steering oar to Typhis and went forward to watch the water ahead in the winding channel.

We heard a last cheer from the quay as the gaulos picked up speed, leaving a triangle of little waves. I looked back and saw many hands waving. I saw Anticlea, her one hand to her mouth, the other holding our Dryas and Anthia. I blew them a kiss. She raised her hand and waved back, then turned to lead the children home. This was my hardest moment. Hers were to come.

V

AHEAD . . . WHAT?

WE WERE SOON OUTSIDE the harbor and headed west across the Galatic Gulf, the apeliotes breeze and the morning sun astern.

Ahead . . . what?

The Pillars of Herakles and Gadeira. Either might be the end. Jason thought he could get us by but warned that Carthaginians were capricious.

"Today they say yes, tomorrow no," he said. "Money is all they understand. We may have to pay them."

The city had provided a leather sack of obols, the coins engraved with the crab, Artemis' symbol; our newer Artemis coins and older drachmae; and Philip's gold staters, each worth twenty-four obols. Another sack held trinkets of elektron jewelry and bronze and silver. Jason urged me to keep this all hidden. "If they find out what you have, they will take everything. If we have to pay, just bring up a few obols and say that is all we have. Say you do not understand them."

Such thoughts seemed out of place. The sun put winter far away. The sea was calm. The light land breeze continued, even rose a little. We sailed easily. The men lashed everything on deck and below. We seemed to be off to a good start.

"Wait," Jason counseled. "Things change quickly." We did have an easy one-day sail across our Galatic Gulf to Rhodai, passing Rhodanus at the mouth of the Rhodanus River. We anchored at Rhodai only for the crew to stow cargo better. We all got a good sleep in the harbor, then sailed at daybreak, out into the Sardoö Pelago, the western half of Our Sea.

Pytheas is warned that pirates hide in the big islands to the east, Ichnussa (Sardinia) and Alalia (Corsica), and that they cruise and raid to the west.

The wind moved to the west, still off the land, and picked up. There were white crests, but we were close enough to shore and the waves did not get big. We now wanted to head south, and Jason had his first test of the wide planks on the bottom. He found we could go south easily, with the sails, both the main and the little artemon on the bowsprit, pulled around to keep full.

"See," he said, "we do not slide."

We were cutting along parallel to the waves. But as the day passed the wind strengthened and shifted southwest. Jason had to ease us more to the east. He pulled the forward edge of the mainsail to make a triangle, the after edge a wind-scooping funnel. The waves got bigger and a few broke over the bow to send water down the deck. Gusts down from the mountains pushed us over until the sea lapped the deck. The wind followed us around and soon was from the south. We had to head almost east.

"I do not like this," Jason said.

"Are we in danger?" I asked. I still did not believe what Pasias had often told me—that a small boat could be as safe as a big one, sometimes safer.

"Not the boat. This is not much. But going east puts us back toward where the pirates work. They hide in those big islands Ichnussa and Alalia. I do not want to meet them again."

"But Ichnussa and Alalia are still quite a way east," I said.

"Pirates move fast. We have to watch for them all the time, even to the Pillars. Many a sailor is a Maurusian slave in Libya because he thought he was safe. And the Maurusians aren't the only pirates."

Luckily the wind continued swinging and soon was from southeast. We now could head almost south again, although pounding into waves slowed us.

At sunset the wind fell to a gentle breeze, even more easterly, and we sailed easily all night. Jason had divided his crew, six men tending, six asleep. I wondered how the six could sleep so quickly, especially when pirates might be anywhere.

"Sailors sleep any time, on any bed," Jason said. He gave the steering oar to Typhis and went to a pallet. "You sleep now, too," he added. "Tomorrow may be good, may be bad."

I was surprised how well I slept, the thin straw pallet barely softening the planking. I awoke stiff and wet with dew but rested, any pirate threat forgotten. Jason I found had been up half the night, so that Typhis could sleep. Now Jason looked around the horizon, gave the oar back to Typhis, and soon was asleep again.

We were well out from land. I could see only tips of mountains in the morning sun. The light wind was still in the east. Leonidas the cook made a breakfast of wheat gruel which we covered with olive blossom honey from Attica–Meton's treat! That and a small cup of wine started our day.

Toward mid-morning, with the sun warming us all, Herakles, who had been watching all around, spoke to Typhis, then awoke Jason. Herakles pointed to the eastern horizon. I saw a tiny dark spot.

"A sail," Jason said. "Watch it."

The spot grew larger and after an hour, Jason said, "The Maurusians."

"The pirates?" I asked.

"Yes. Looks like the ones that caught us last year."

"Can't we outrun him?"

"Not with this gaulos. See, he is both rowing and sailing. Twice as fast as we ever could."

"But the land is not far. Couldn't we find a harbor?"

"That's what he wants. He pinned us against the land last time. We could only drive on the rocks or fight. I do not make that mistake twice."

I did not distract Jason further. He, Typhis, and Herakles talked rapidly. Others joined. None seemed afraid, despite what all must have remembered.

The galley came on rapidly. Now I could see his swelling sail and the oars, eight to a side, pulling strongly. We were sailing south. He was heading west. As he came closer, I could see the ugly ramming beak rise out of the waves. The galley looked about the same length as our gaulos.

We sailed on. The Maurusian captain must have thought we did not see him. He kept his course to meet us at a right angle, to ram, impale our boat, board, loot, and kill any who did not surrender into slavery. Then the galley would back off and let our gaulos sink.

Jason kept our course, with the wind behind the Maurusian and to our left. He had a man fasten a line to the lower right corner of our mainsail and lead it to the deck inside the stays from the mast-top to the side of the boat. The line was left slack, with the sail still pulling on the original line outside the stays.

The Maurusian pirate galley.

Leonidas went below for a clay pot half-full of pitch. When Jason nodded, he scooped still-glowing charcoal from the cooking firebox into the pot. He and Herakles stuffed rags, straw, and wood shavings on top. Herakles stood at our prow with the pot at his feet. In his belt was a hand-axe and his knife. He kept his right arm around the swan's-neck timber, the hand on his axe.

In two hours the pirate had come within a few stadia. We could see the helmsman steering skillfully. At the prow were shouting men, their swords, knives, and spears gleaming. I knew a little of their language. It was clear that if they got aboard, there would be no one to tell Massalia. I stood near Jason.

The galley came on. I saw no escape. He would ram us just where he wanted to. I could only suppose that Jason had chosen to die fighting. He had handed me a knife.

When ten seconds would have laid the gaulos across the beak, Jason shouted. He and Typhis swung our big steering oars and the men hauled our mainsail in on the right side, as far as the yard would go. One man hauled in quickly on the new line while another released the original, and the sail's lower corner was drawn in almost to the center of the boat. Another man hauled down the yard at its forward end and drew up brails to make the sail a triangle again. Still another flattened the artemon.

The gaulos turned in a tight arc, almost into the wind.

In an instant we were parallel to the galley, five or six cubits away. The pirate helmsman tried to turn. The oarmaster swung his whip to make the slave rowers back oars.

It was too late. The galley could not stop or turn enough. Our prow hit the oars on his right side and snapped them, one by one. We heard the screams of the slaves and could see them thrown about, their chains flailing. The oarmaster was felled by a broken oar butt.

Just as the middle section passed our prow, Herakles hurled the now blazing pitch pot. It shattered against the galley mast. The mess landed on a grass matting shelter. That was quickly afire and flames rose to the sail.

Jason had veered the gaulos to scrape alongside. Herakles leaped aboard the galley and ran to the helmsman. The pirate drew his dagger but Herakles was too quick. He seized the man, raised him high, and threw him down on his head on our foredeck. With his axe Herakles then cut the two ropes from a cross-beam at the back of the galley to the mast-top. The mast fell. The burning sail dropped on screaming pirates and slaves.

In these seconds we had drifted apart, too far for Herakles to jump back. He ran forward, grabbed three pirates who had crawled aft from the flames, and threw them one by one into the sea. They were in terror between the flames and this raging Tartessan giant. He threw the unconscious oarmaster after them. Four slaves whose benches were clear of the fire cried to Herakles. He jerked their chains from the benches and pointed to the gaulos. The men jumped and swam, despite their chains.

Then Herakles followed. Two men he had thrown over tried to stop him. He smashed their heads together, pushed them under, and swam free. One did not come up. The other fled.

We were dead in the water. Jason had kept our sails trimmed flat to hold us almost into the wind. Herakles came alongside, holding to a broken oar blade. A sailor dropped a stout rope. Herakles knotted it around himself and five sailors pulled him aboard. Ropes then were dropped to the slaves and Herakles himself pulled each aboard.

Jason quickly put us back on course to the south. To the east, the galley drifted, to burn and sink or wash upon the rocky shore. I hoped the rest of the slaves had died quickly and mercifully and that the pirates had suffered agonies to the end. We could not have saved the other slaves and we would not have saved the pirates.

Jason gave the steering oar to Typhis and walked forward to see the Maurusian Herakles had thrown aboard. Herakles stood astride the body, ready to stamp or kick. But the man was dead.

I went with Jason. He rolled the man over and smiled. Almost a smile of triumph, however bitter.

"He tried to kill me the other time."

"The gods do hand out justice sometimes," I said.

"I do not know about justice," Jason said. "I do know this will make it easier at Gadeira. We will give them his body. Those slaves are Carthaginians. We will take them to Gadeira."

At supper I tried to praise Jason. His helmsmanship and the skill of his crew, most of all of Herakles, had saved us. Herakles blew on the blisters on his right arm and hand, doused them with olive oil, and smiled behind his singed beard. He had enjoyed himself.

Jason filled his mouth with beans and said, "We were lucky."

VI

TO GADEIRA

JASON KEPT US far out in the Sardoö Pelago on to the Pillars. He did not want to meet Carthaginians. Nor did he want to stop at Meloussa, Kromyoussa, or others of the islands off Iberia.

We rounded Iberia's southeastern cape and Jason said, "Mainaké is not much farther. But we will not stop unless somebody makes us."

That was fine. We had plenty to eat and drink, even for our freed slaves, and the gaulos was sailing well. Jason, getting the feel better, found he could maneuver even more closely than when we met the pirates. "The timbers on the bottom serve us well," was his only comment. "Also the big steering oars."

We got past Mainaké. As the last port before the Pillars, it might have had a Carthaginian picket cruising nearby. But the Carthaginians must have felt secure at the Pillars.

Early next afternoon Jason had the sails furled and put the men to rowing slowly.

"We pass the Pillars at night," Jason explained. "They have a base there."

After sunset Jason raised sail. An easterly breeze moved us, and the men rowed to keep up speed. There was a little light with the waning moon not yet risen, and the huge rock Kalpé on the northern side looked menacing. It was indeed a pillar that only our ancient Herakles could have put there.

Jason kept us close to the Libyan coast. "Over there," he said, pointing

---

The ship passes the Balearic islands of Meloussa (Minorca) and Kromyoussa (Mallorca) and reaches the Pillars of Herakles, Kalpé (Gibraltar) and Abyla (Apes' Hill, Ceuta). In the shadow of Kalpé is Herakleia (Carteya, Spain).

The gaulos sailing oceanward past the Pillars of Herakles.

toward Kalpé, "we once had a great sea base in that bay – Herakleia. Now it's their guard port. We keep away."

To our left dimly rose the other pillar, Abyla. "Besides," he added, "we pick up a good current in here. Okeanos flows in, but for two or three hours after high tide at Kalpé, the water flows westward along the shore. Out in the middle we would have to fight it."

I had heard of tides, a little. I would have to ask Jason more when he was less busy watching for landmarks to our left, Carthaginians to our right, and keeping clear of shoals.

Jason found his current. Even after the breeze failed, the men kept us moving easily, and at last we were out. Jason relaxed at daybreak, and headed us northwest, about thirty stadia off the Iberian coast. Our gaulos rose to the swells of Okeanos, a different feeling for me. These were greater than I had ever seen. The wind continued light and the water itself seemed smooth. But often we could not see the coast from between swells.

"A storm far out west," Jason explained. "Let it stay there." I agreed. I wanted no gruel that morning. Leonidas handed me my bowl and said, "Eat." I said, "No." He said, "Eat."

"Do as he says," Jason laughed. "You will feel better even if you lose it."

I tried, but set the bowl aside and turned to watch the coast, the only fixed line to be seen. But it disappeared too often. I closed my eyes. Herakles tilted my bowl into his own mouth. His appetite matched his size.

Slowly we sailed the six hundred stadia from the Pillars to Gadeira. The fair notus breeze followed us. It was another spring morning to make everyone glad–except me. I felt no better at noon, nor at supper. Leonidas was scornful. Jason's sympathy was diluted by his watch for landmarks.

Toward sunset he sighted the statue of Kronos at the mouth of the Gadeira harbor. A Greek god, an old bearded man, one hand stretching to the south and holding a key, guarding a Carthaginian port! We had erected it when King Arganthonios ruled Tartessos, to honor our god of time and Tartessos' god-founder Gargoris. The Carthaginians found it a useful mark for ships.

It was dark when Jason eased us into the harbor and to an open space at a quay. We could hear carousing in taverns, but nobody saw us. My stomach settled.

Jason had wrapped the Maurusian pirate's now stiff body in sail-cloth and slung it over the lee side. It gave off strong odors. Now Herakles hoisted it to the quay and laid it out. The breeze was off the sea, which made us thankful.

Except for Jason and the youngest sailor, the boy Eban, the men slipped ashore and disappeared, as sailors do. They returned before dawn, quietly. Tartessans did not roister in Gadeira. Jason kept the freed slaves aboard. He wanted them to back his story to port officers in the morning.

As we ate our breakfast gruel, a soldier came. Jason talked to him in Carthaginian and pointed to the body. The soldier left.

"I told him to bring his captain," Jason said. "You stay on the boat. I may bring him aboard but I hope not." He sent Leonidas below for a small amphora of wine. "If it is the captain I hope it is, wine will explain for us."

It must have been. The soldier returned with a fat man who clearly enjoyed his comforts and thought this an early hour. Jason waved to Leonidas, and two cups of wine were handed ashore. The captain's face brightened and his cup was soon empty. Leonidas took the amphora ashore and kept the cup full. Jason only sipped.

The captain knelt down and opened the sail-cloth wrapping, took one look, and closed the cloth quickly. I thought for a moment he would lose his wine. He sent the soldier away. He and Jason talked, with much pointing to the body and to our gaulos. Jason's gestures told the story of the fight and the fire. I did not try to hide, but the captain seemed little aware of me. As Jason had hoped, the wine was doing our work.

Jason called the freed slaves ashore and handed them over to the captain, who questioned them briefly. The soldier returned with several other men. They carried the body into the city.

The captain now was laughing with Jason. Finally he walked slowly back into the city. He stepped carefully, with the slaves following.

Jason came back. He was glad but cautious.

"So much for that," he said. "He was glad the pirate was dead and his galley destroyed. I told him you were a passenger from Rhodai bound for Mainaké and we had come here first to tell the news."

"But what will he do when he finds out we are going the other way?" I asked. Deception was not easy for me.

"Tomorrow he will not remember what I said," Jason laughed. "By the time anybody starts thinking, we will be far gone."

Jason spent little time at the quay. He asked me for money and went in for dried figs and other fruit. He also sent Herakles and Leonidas in, who soon returned with a coil of thick rope. "We never have enough. We may have to anchor in deep water somewhere."

A number of Gadeirans saw us. Jason spoke to a few. They were sailors and fishermen, and probably Tartessans or of Tartessan stock. A few girls came down, but Jason waved them away. Herakles shook his head sadly.

In an hour we cast off and rowed out. Kronos soon saw us heading northwest, our sail catching the still following wind. Jason gave the steering oar to Typhis and went to his pallet.

"You got us by, Jason," I said as I went to mine for at least a nap before the swells began again.

"We were lucky," he said again.

VII

A TARTESSAN HERITAGE

I SOON FELT QUEASY, but when Leonidas served our noon meal of cheese and dried fish and added the figs, I forced myself to eat a little. I found Jason was right.

"See?" Jason said, "Food heals everything at sea."

"I will not be greedy," I replied.

We sailed on, in sight of the coast. Jason knew every hill and valley. Soon we passed low marshy land around the mouths of the Tartessos River. Jason told me that a day's sail up that river was Tharsis, a great city which was once the Tartessan capital. He pointed to a tower at the mouth—"The Tower of Geryon, one of our gods."

"How soon do we turn north for the Hyperborean lands?" I asked. I did not realize how long the Iberian coast was.

"A few days yet. First we go into another old Tartessan harbor. It will not delay us. We must do things for the ship that we dared not take time for at Gadeira. And I want to go up to Illipla to talk to my grandfather. He has been to some of those lands. The men all live around here. It has been a year since they last saw any kin. My grandfather must think I am dead—if he is still alive. And we will get more food."

At sunset he sighted his marks. The breeze carried us toward a wide inlet that looked more part of the sea. I saw scattered sandbars and wondered how we could miss them all.

The ship passes the mouth of the Tartessos River (the Guadalquivir), which flows past Tharsis (Sevilla), a day's sail, one hundred kilometers or sixty miles, upstream. Just up the Urium River from the sea, on the right bank, is a ruined fortress or temple, the site nearly two thousand years later of the monastery at La Rábida, where Christopher Columbus was to be consoled during his long effort to get royal backing for this first voyage of discovery, from Palos, just beyond. The monastery is still there and active.

With Typhis steering, Jason went to the prow to call back course changes. I went to watch. "These bars move all the time," he said.

"Why?" I asked.

"Tides," he replied. "Twice a day the sea flows in, twice a day out. It moves the bars one way and another. Storms too. And the water in here gets deeper or shallower with each tide."

Tides again. And again, Jason was too busy to explain. I had heard of a well at Gadeira that rose and fell with tides and would ask about that too.

The inlet divided about thirty stadia from the open sea, at a low sandy point. "The Luxium River," Jason said pointing to the left branch. "We go up the Urium." He headed us past a bluff with a ruined temple or fort on the right bank. The breeze died and the men rowed us toward a settlement beyond. We were soon at a small quay. "In our great time," Jason said, "this was our main port." Across the Urium and really on the bank of the Luxium was the bigger town Jason called Onuba. "They ship metals from the mines and grain from the mills. Only shippers and money-lenders there. Rich houses. Tartessans live here and must get permission to go to Onuba."

I was content at our quay. I wanted to talk to no one in Onuba. Anyone hearing of our venture would oppose it.

The men went ashore. Jason and Eban stayed with me. "It will be safer with me here," Jason said.

"Don't you want to see your families?" I asked.

"Eban has no one. My family is all up at Illipla. I go there tomorrow. I stay here tonight. Somebody from Onuba may come to find out what strange boat this is. It was still light enough when we came in."

"What will you tell them? You can't use that Mainaké story again."

"The truth. I lost my boat to pirates and I now sail this."

No one came. In the morning he went into the settlement and returned with a friend who showed him a small open boat. "I can sail to Illipla in this," Jason explained. "The gaulos needs water too deep." He left me with Eban, with instructions to plead ignorance if anybody questioned us. "Tell them I will be back tomorrow." He sailed off alone.

Jason returned late the next day. He and the crew spent the rest of that day and all the next working on rigging. They replaced lines that showed wear and tightened any that were slack. "It is easy here," Jason said. "At sea a parted line is trouble. Any place a rope touches anything, even another rope, it wears."

Jason spread the sails on a field. He went over them stitch by stitch, as at Massalia. He sewed in a few patches. He made pockets along the vertical edges and inserted smooth sticks.

The men brought aboard more food. I asked if they needed money. Jason replied that they had their own way of paying among their people.

"If we give them even obols," he said, "the Carthaginians will take them and torture the people to make them tell how they hid the food they gave us."

Jason carefully went over the right side of the gaulos for damage from our pirate fight. He found only scratches and one large scrape where the two boats came together for Herakles' leap. Rubbing with a rough flat stone smoothed the marks. Meanwhile, I set up my gnomon ashore to measure the angle of the sun, counted the days back to equinox, and found we were about five degrees south of Massalia's latitude. I saw the boy Eban, busy as he was, watching me.

After all was as Jason wanted it, we carried amphorae to the village well. "The best water along the Urium," Jason said. "I have drunk it far at sea."

The well was about ten stadia from the quay, with a deep-worn path between. As we approached, a man sitting under a tree watched. I thought, a Carthaginian and trouble. Then I saw his clothes were ragged and his feet were bare. He was old.

We came close and he stood up.

"Am I too old and weak?" he asked. Jason embraced him. He handed Jason a tiny lamp, an Attic lamp, and a scroll. "I left everything else," he said.

"Girondas, my grandfather," Jason told me. "I would not let him join us because he was too old and weak. Now he is with us."

The old man, full of speechless joy, helped fill amphorae and would have taken mine if I had let him. He carried everything he owned in a sheepskin to be his bed aboard.

We returned to the gaulos. Herakles was last aboard, again carrying two amphorae, and a live young goat around his neck, bleating against fate. The goat he tethered to the mast and went back for all the fodder he could carry. What the goat did not live to eat would soften a pallet.

"Tonight we sail," Jason announced. "The tide will be right. We should get away without being seen. If not, we are for Gadeira."

An hour after sunset, the ebbing tide stretched our mooring ropes. Herakles pushed us from the quay and jumped aboard, the gaulos rocking with his great weight.

A light breeze followed us down to the marshes of the inlet. We heard no challenge. We stopped halfway out, and Herakles waded ashore for cakes of salt left by tidal pools. The salt would be useful if we caught fish, or might be traded. Salt is as good as money to many people.

"How far to the Sacred Capes?" I asked again as we lost the darkened shore.

"About one thousand stadia," Jason replied. "Two days' sail, maybe three, maybe a week. The gods know, yours and ours, we don't."

I should have been impatient, but Jason had taught me that impatience changed nothing at sea. Already I was farther from Our Sea than any Greek before me – even Kolaeus – unless Odysseus really wandered this far seeking the City of the Dead.

I was on Okeanos. The swell was gentle now. Whatever storm had made the big swells had died. I lay on my pallet. Girondas slept soundly and happily beside me. Typhis was at the steering oar. Jason slept. Five crewmen slept, five others tended sails or kept lookout. Some sang softly.

I wanted to tell my Anticlea how wonderful it was, how much I longed for her and Dryas and Anthia. Perhaps the quarter moon shone my thoughts to her. I tried to calculate the angle of the moonbeams between here and Massalia. If I could do that, I would know how far we were west of Massalia in degrees, in stadia if I knew Earth's circumference. I fell asleep on the problem.

VIII

TO THE SACRED CAPES

I AWOKE in two hours to find us in a rising sea, the wind southwest. The deck was wet and the air cold. The gaulos was sailing well, with the main yard hauled down at the forward end and the sail a triangle close to the right side, the artemon flat, but the waves slowed us. Often a big one almost stopped us.

Jason was steering, Girondas beside him. I thought the old man should be below for shelter, but he shivered less than I. He watched the dim coast to our right and before long saw what he and Jason were looking for–the mouth of a river.

"The Anas," Jason said. "This blow came up suddenly and we are too close to shore."

He and Girondas found the entrance and we soon were in calm water. The gaulos was nosed into a bank, and Herakles and others went overboard to prop timbers against our sides.

"When the tide goes out," Jason explained, "we will be on the bottom. The timbers will keep us from falling over."

Again, waiting. The wind became a gale and I was glad not to be out. As the tide fell after daylight, the gaulos sat upright on her new vertical bottom timbers and stilts.

"What if the water does not come back?" I asked Jason, only half joking. I still little understood tides, and here in six hours' time the river was six cubits lower.

The ship takes storm refuge in the Anas River, known today as the Guadiana which in its lower reaches is the boundary between Spain and Portugal. Pytheas is reminded of a predicted conjunction of Selene the moon and the planet Ares (Mars). They pass Cyneticum (Portugal's Cabo Santa María near Faro) on the way to the Sacred Capes. He is told about the rough Gulf of Oestrymnis (the Bay of Biscay) and its great sailors.

"Then we wait forever," Jason laughed. "Don't worry, it will come back, especially with this onshore wind. Anyway, in two weeks the moon will be full and the tide higher than ever."

"What *has* the moon to do with tides?" I asked.

"I do not know. But the highest and lowest tides come with full and new moons. The moon must pull them up and down more then. Down when it is on the other side of the world."

So Jason too felt that the moon went around us. He had told me long before that all sailors who had thought about it knew that the world had to be a ball. "How else would shores ahead be first just a line, then rise up to hills when we get to them?"

I asked then if he had seen an eclipse of the moon or sun, with a circular shadow passing across.

"Yes," he replied. "And our Tartessan wise men of so long ago knew what the shadow meant and when one was coming. We have not lost all their wisdom."

The men used the low tide to inspect the gaulos' hull. They waded in the mud and with sharp shells scraped off sea grass and little shellfish. They melted more pitch and daubed it along seams.

"Always something to do around a boat," Jason said.

I too found something. Jason had showed me Girondas' scroll, a sketch map of the Iberian coastline from the Pillars around the Sacred Capes, north to another cape where the shore turned eastward as far as it had run north. North of that cape were dots for islands that must be the Cassiterides. Our own periplus only hinted at some of this. He had made the sketch on his forced voyages for the Carthaginians.

"I knew the way from what my grandfather learned from his grandfather," Girondas explained in Greek, a language he seemed to know well. "The Carthaginians gave me my freedom for showing them."

His sketch, set beside my own, made it appear that where Iberia turned east must be about as far north from here as Massalia. He came below and I asked how far east the Iberian coast ran before turning north again.

"I am not sure," he admitted. "The seas up there are very stormy. On some voyages it takes weeks, on others only a few days. It may be four thousand stadia, maybe five."

I would make sure of the latitude there. I wished again for a way to discover east-west distances. I had long known of a predicted spring conjunction of Selene and Ares, the red wandering star, and now it seemed

salted them ashore on racks, then brought them home. But not all came home. Only the bravest and the best even tried."

Again, something to think about as we boarded the gaulos and the men rowed us out to sea.

The waves were small under the big cliffs, but around the cape, we found ourselves in a fresh breeze and choppy seas. Jason unfurled the sail and we kept a westerly course, the closest possible to the wind without slowing us. The Cape of the Cynetes and Promontorium Sacrum dropped lower and lower on the horizon, with the afternoon sun glinting off their red rocks. It was a spectacle that must be welcome to any sailor coming from whatever he had sought in the west. I felt, after hearing Girondas, that men had been using Okeanos' western reaches for many centuries.

If there were monsters and terrors out in those mists, as the Carthaginians and their sires the Phoenicians said, there were men to subdue them, and not always Carthaginians or Phoenicians.

"The sea stops nobody who wants to go," Girondas said. "It takes him."

IX

UP THE IBERIAN COAST

THE WIND in time shifted back southwest and Jason turned us northerly, bearing in toward the coast.

"Now we are headed for your Hyperborean lands," he said. "From here we use the sun and stars more than ever."

"If what I have studied is true," I said, "the farther north we get, the more the stars will change. Some will never set and we will see them going around those three stars so close together that move around that empty spot near the end of Cynosura, a sort of missing corner to a square in the heavens."

"Those three will keep us heading north," Jason agreed. "I have used them many times."

Our life became a round of small duties. Jason and Typhis spelled each other at steering. Herakles helped if extra strength was needed. Leonidas prepared meals. Girondas slept much but awoke quickly when any change in the motion of the boat told him he might be useful. He helped haul in or slack sail ropes. He led in songs to help the men pull, or to row. He even took the steering oar at times. If Girondas was frail, he

---

Pytheas mentions the "polar square," three stars and an empty spot over our North Pole then, before Polaris became our North Star. The three included [Beta] Ursae Minoris and [Alpha] Draconis, near the tail of Cynosura, our Little Bear or Little Dipper. The ship passes Promontorium Ophiussae (Portugal's Cabo Roca), and the mouth of the Tagus River, with Olispo (Lisboa), its harbor city, then the Durium (the Douro River), and heads for Oestrymnis (Finisterre). After the storm it passes La Coruña, with the Tower of Herakles on the rocky shore nearby, and finds harbor at El Ferrol in Artabria (Galicia).

The Alione (Basque) captain tells of ocean currents helping ships to reach our Grand Banks: either the west-flowing Irminger Current passing south of Iceland, or more easily the Canaries Current past the Madeira and Canary Islands, then the North Equatorial Current to the Caribbean archipelago, and the Gulf Stream up our East Coast; finally, the North Atlantic Drift and the prevailing westerlies helping them home.

masked it. His hand was steady and our course straight. (Once I tried to spell Jason. Our wake soon looked like a snake. "You work too hard at it," Jason laughed.)

In about two days we saw the shore again and Jason sailed parallel, one hundred or more stadia off. We could just see a headland Jason called Ophiussae.

"There is a big river out of Lusitania and a good harbor at Olispo in there," he said, "but two or three more days will put us near some big inlets, then we can either round Oestrymnis and go into the Gulf of Oestrymnis, or head north until the coast comes out to meet us again, with islands called the Oestrymnides."

Thinking of Girondas' report of men along Iberia's northern shore who told of a land far to the west, I urged Jason to turn east at the cape.

"If the weather is right," he said. "There are terrible storms."

"I know, Girondas told me. If we can't do it now, maybe on the way home. I would like to talk to men he told about."

"They are great sailors," Jason said. "Tartessans used to meet them in far places. The Carthaginians sent a ship under a man named Himilco up here not long after they conquered us to look for cassiterite. But he went no farther. He told of great hardships. Tartessans had long traded with the Oestrymnians and to the islands on north. I don't know what he found hard.

"They tried to keep his voyage a secret, I guess because he found little. Only some cassiterite in northwestern Iberia, not where most of it comes from. He claimed to have gone to the Cassiterides but nobody believed him. We all knew about it and had good laughs. Even slaves can laugh."

A wind shift to the northwest forced Jason to head back southwest to keep off the shore. As the wind swung around, we had found ourselves headed closer and closer to the beaches and soon could see breakers. The men quickly and easily shifted the sails while Typhis and Herakles worked the steering oars.

"I thought I saw a river," I said to Jason. "Why not go in?"

"Better to stay out of the Durium. A bad storm is making up. We want plenty of sea between us and the shore. I know, we went in at the Anas, but we knew those waters better. It has been a long time since we saw this coast."

In another three hours the storm was upon us with fury we rarely saw on Our Sea. We sailed as long as we could, and with the wind luckily mostly out of the north, could edge farther offshore.

Jason reduced the mainsail by half, then had it wrapped tightly around the yard and lowered to the deck. He put up the small storm sail he had made at Massalia on the after side of the mast, and took in the artemon. The boat steadied somewhat and he and Typhis could keep it moving southwest. They acted as one man swinging the long oar on the lee side. Herakles stood by.

Waves smashed us about. Many grew taller than our mast—twice as tall, I was sure—and in the trough, our storm sail hung limp. When we rose to a crest, it filled with a loud clap. Jason had it taken in just before sunset.

Now we drifted. The men, who had worked as a team, each knowing what the others had done and sensing what Jason shouted, now clung to solid timbers, to move warily to whatever had to be done next. Some lashed themselves to the mast, but always ready to jump to any need. Jason told me to lash myself out of the way.

He ordered all our heavy rope, including the new coil bought at Gadeira, streamed over the stern in big bights. This kept our stern to the seas, and we drifted downwind slowly, with less violent heaving. Pasias' men had built this gaulos well. The stern with its little poop deck and helmsman's shelter rose easily to all but the steepest waves that looked like cliffs. Much spray came aboard, little solid water.

Jason and Herakles had hauled in the lee steering oar and lashed it on deck, the other already secured. Their only awareness of the cold that now had me shaking violently was to put on the sodden clothes they had shed while fighting the oar. They were then as wet with sweat as with spray.

Herakles and Typhis went below to make sure stores and cargo were secure. Leonidas went with them and came back with crusts of bread—our supper for that wild night. He reported some stone ballast had shifted, there was water, and Herakles and Typhis needed help. Jason sent four more men. How anybody could see anything, much less move stone ballast, was more than I could imagine. But I knew these men had been through this many times.

Leonidas handed me a crust and I ate it. The great swells of our first days on Okeanos had enabled me to endure these seas. Or so I thought.

As wave after wave, crest foaming, hissing, thundering, lifted then dropped us, I felt queasy again. I remembered what Pasias had said . . . there would be times to wonder what in the world I was doing out there . . . and found myself leaning overside, wet and miserable, clinging with numb hands to rigging.

I thought of Girondas and looked about. He must be suffering. And he was. He was close to me. "The first storm always gets me," he gasped. "Then no more." I hoped for as much. He was as wet as I and must have been as cold, but he was not shaking. The next time I opened my eyes, he was gone.

Overside, I thought in panic! But I looked back and saw him and Jason talking in shouts. Then Girondas too went below.

I noticed our deck canting to the right and knew something must be off center below. Trying to be at least as strong as Girondas, I scrambled to Jason and asked if I could help.

"Stay here," he said. "You might get hurt. They will get things right."

The men did. (On a calm day I looked about the hold and wondered how a half dozen men could have done anything. "They knew what to do," was all Jason could tell me.)

Slowly they got the gaulos to an even keel. Herakles then passed up a large jar to be dumped on deck. I had supposed the water in the hold had flowed in from the deck but also wondered if there had been damage. I had heard sailors talking on the Massalia quays about "seams starting" and now I knew what that might mean here.

After dozens of jars-full had been dumped, Herakles came to Jason. He was very tired. He seemed to assure Jason that things were in better shape below. He stayed on deck while Jason made his own inspection.

One by one the men came up, all as tired as Herakles, some with bloody hands and arms. One came up naked. Jason followed and gave him his own outer robe, soaked as it was, and the man wrapped himself and lay in a corner to rest.

"A plank is split," Jason shouted to me. "He tore up his clothes to jam into it."

That had to hold until we got to a harbor.

Leonidas and Girondas stayed below the rest of that weary, dreary night to watch for more ballast shifts and leaks. If Girondas was as sick as I, his time below must have been awful, but I knew he would complain to no one. As clean a ship as Jason kept, the hold still accumulated odors.

With dawn the storm began to ease, and by mid-morning the wind had dropped to a breeze. The waves were still high but more regular and smooth-crested and we could sail westward, with the yard again drawn down at the forward end to make the mainsail a triangle. The sun warmed us all and Jason let everybody rest as much as possible on the drying deck. Typhis shared the steering oar with Jason, each taking an hour or so. Herakles lay relaxed and snored loudly. His body swayed on his muscles with the movement of the deck. Girondas likewise slept. You would never have thought he had been sick. The men awake wrung out their wet robes and hung in the rigging what they were not wearing. So did I. I thought of heavy clothing I had brought for northern regions, but decided to endure a little discomfort. The men had forgotten theirs.

When Leonidas came with bread and cheese, I tried to eat, then handed it back. If I had ever gained sea legs, I had lost them. Later, as the seas eased, I remembered how much better I felt after eating that other time, and asked Leonidas for another piece of bread. I did feel better.

"We will make a sailor out of you yet," Jason laughed.

"Maybe even a Tartessan," said Typhis.

"Then he will have to dance in the streets of Massalia." Jason could joke about it now.

The wind kept us heading to the west, then backed to northwest and we could steer northeast. During the night Jason and Typhis kept the polar square off our left side, halfway from the mast-top to the prow. "I hope we come out close to Oestrymnis," Jason said. "There is a good harbor on beyond. We can beach the boat."

I tried unsuccessfully to get at least a rough angle reading from the polar square with my cross-staff. During our passage from the Sacred Capes I had practiced snap sights of the sun, trying to guess closely just when the mast, my gnomon at sea, was vertical, then counting the circular marks I had painted on deck to the number touched by the noon shadow. I now tried this despite the much greater motion of the gaulos, with a series of angles just before and after noon. Young Eban put his foot on the mark the shadow reached when I called, "Now!"

I must have gained some skill. After I had made the calculations, the angle readings averaged out to put us around forty degrees north of the equator. I also timed the length of day fairly well with close attention by myself and by Girondas to the hourglass, and found it to be nearly fourteen hours. This confirmed the celestial readings. Jason was pleased.

"If so and if we are not farther offshore than I think," he said, "we should be headed right."

"How can you even guess how far offshore?" I asked. "I lost all sense of where we were in that storm."

"I just feel it," he smiled.

I was also as pleased as Jason at something else – beardless Eban, who could not have been more than half my age and more likely younger, and who had helped so on my rough gnomon work with the mast, kept on watching Girondas and me and asking Girondas many questions, some of which he had to translate for me to answer. An apt pupil makes any teacher feel good.

Jason held us to a steady northeastward course, and in time we began to sight birds. "Those do not go far from land," Jason said. "We will see it in the morning – if we are still lucky."

During the night I heard the crew stirring and awoke to see them shortening sail again, as they had early in the storm. Girondas had gotten up to help and when he returned to his pallet, I asked if another storm was coming. "No, we are just slowing down. We do not want to get inshore until daylight shows us where we are." I could see nothing. I was happy to trust the Tartessan sea-sense and went back to sleep.

Sunrise came to us about thirty stadia off the coast. All studied the shore. It seemed very irregular, with several high headlands that could be islands or peninsulas between big inlets or rivers.

"I think we are about a day's sail from Oestrymnis," Jason said at last. "The coast turns northeastward at Cape Nerium and a big harbor is another day's sail beyond. If this wind holds."

The wind did hold, even moved westerly to give us easy going. In his two days, Jason took us into this big harbor. "We do not always make my guesses look so good," Jason said.

There were settlements about the harbor and Jason and Typhis steered past a tall tower on shore to a beach in a big cove on the north side. There we would be safe from almost all winds. We arrived at high tide and they placed the gaulos parallel to a beach as close in as it would go. When the keel touched, the men laid out anchors from each end, and brought up amphorae of wine, water, and olive oil and put them ashore. "They would spill when we careen," Jason explained.

A term I had not heard. As the tide ebbed, the gaulos, steadied by a line from the mast-top to Herakles ashore, eased down on its land side.

The Tower of Herakles, near La Coruña, Spain, as seen from the sea.

As soon as the water had dropped below the split plank, all went overside. I went with them, to hold tools or run errands.

"I was afraid of that," Jason said after inspection. "The plank did not split from the working of the ship. We must have hit a log. There were enough bumps."

The plank was split for more than a cubit, and so were the ones above and below it. The sailor's torn clothing still held in the cracks, but the damage called for rebuilding. Luckily, all was close to the water line and not much lead sheathing had to be pulled back.

"We will be here maybe a week," Jason said. "Take ashore anything you don't want to get wet. When the tide comes up, the boat will fill."

Everybody went to work. By the time the tide had started flooding, they had cut away the damage and found one frame inside cracked.

When work had to stop, Girondas, Typhis, and several others wandered away. Many boats, some like ours, but more of them different, were in the cove and elsewhere. There would be sailors to talk to, people ashore to give information, and, our men no doubt knew, women to be told tales from Our Sea.

I had taken my hourglass, water-clock, cross-staff, journal, periplus, and map ashore, along with Girondas' map. I also took my gnomon to a flat place to await the noon sun. The sun did not look likely. Jason had said that it rained much of the time in Artabria, as he called this country.

The men took the sails ashore for shelter over stores, and over me while I studied and wrote my journal. I felt that even if we got no farther, I would have much to tell.

After an hour or so, a small boy came running along the beach. "Beetas, Beetas," he shouted. Jason talked to him in a Keltoi tongue.

"He wants you," Jason called to me. "Girondas sent him."

I followed the boy back. He chattered away. My limited Keltoi could not keep up with his dialect. I tried to thank him but he only stared at me and went on talking. I gave him an obol and he squealed and hugged me as high as he could reach.

He led me a few stadia to a quay. There were Girondas, Typhis, and men from a large sailing ship at the quay. The ship was much longer than our gaulos, but not much wider. It appeared built for speed, with square sails furled on three masts, but also for long passages and big cargos. It smelled strongly of fish.

The men were seated around a large flat rock, with cups of wine at hand and a jug in the middle. Girondas arose.

"You wanted to talk to somebody who had gone west across Okeanos? Here is one. He sails tonight if the wind is right."

He introduced the man, bearded and probably as strong as Herakles, as an Alione captain from a port several hundred stadia on east. I wondered at Girondas' ease in this man's language. Jason had told me his grandfather could master almost any dialect, but this sounded stranger than any I had ever heard.

At first the man talked little, partly because of suspicion. But with the help of wine, he told Girondas for me of long voyages to rocky shores with extensive shallows offshore, all teeming with fish.

"How does he get there?" I asked. "Sailing west?"

"Not always," he replied. "The winds come from the west much of the time. They help us coming home but not going."

"I know the westerly winds," Girondas said. "I have fought them around Albion and Ierné. What other way is there?"

"If you are lucky," the Alione said, "you can follow a river in the sea far to the north. But great cold, white, floating mountains may drift down upon you. Bad storms come up quickly. You go by a land of fire, where no one lives, then work southwest for days until you come to these rich waters. The shores are very dangerous, but there are harbors. The sea is often heavy with low clouds that no one can see through."

"If he can't go that way," I asked Girondas, "does he come home?"

"No. There is another way. Much longer, but much easier, and often as fast. We go south first." He took us to a wide spot on the beach, and with a stick drew a rough chart in the sand. A heavy curved north-south line indicated the coast of Iberia. He took a smaller stick and showed a course for a ship, trending more and more southwest, past two groups of islands, then heading west.

"Another river in the sea helps us this way," he explained. "Still another takes us on west. We have fair winds all the way most of the time—although there are often terrible summer storms that smash you one way, then another. But after four or five weeks, we come to more islands. Still another river, a great warm blue one, takes us north along a long, flat coast. It can be very rough if the wind blows from the north, but in time we find ourselves on these same fishing grounds, amid the same clouds, and catching great stores of great fish."

I turned to Girondas and sighed, "I should have brought along parchment to copy this."

"He would cover it over," Girondas said. "He is still not sure of any of us. Just remember."

"Well enough. Ask him how they get home."

"Those westerly winds now bring us home," the captain said. "And that warm river in the sea that brought us up that far coast curves across to help us. It is no longer fast, but it moves us, even if the wind dies. If we could go to those fishing grounds as easily as we usually get home, we would be rich."

He talked on of the fish and the people on the rocky shores. Dark-skinned, he told Girondas, but not like those we knew to live far to the south on the Libyan continent. More copper-colored, and savages, he said, and living on fish and dolphins and whales and on animals on the shore.

When the wine was gone, we returned to our gaulos. Girondas and the other men made themselves useful or rested. I went to the sail shelter and sketched what I remembered of the chart in the sand. I even walked back to see if the Alione had left it but found the lines trampled. As Girondas had said, the man was not sure of me, and science, geography, or astronomy were not in his language, even though he certainly understood the basics of each.

Jason, Herakles, and others at the gaulos had kept busy. A stout new frame had been shaped with an adz to fasten to the damaged one. New sections of plank had been cut with flat, tapered inside ends, ready to be inserted. The sound ends of the good planking left on the hull were to be tapered to match.

Before the tide came up, Jason had the hole stuffed with pallets and anything available–including Girondas' sheepskin–then covered with spare sailcloth to keep out as much water as possible until the tide fell again.

"You will have a wet bed," I told Girondas.

"So will everybody," he laughed. "A sailor sleeps in any bed, or none."

I asked Girondas if he had noticed the Alione captain's bronze knife and other bronze objects here. I saw one man digging with what looked like a bronze shovel. We have long used iron.

"They make bronze up here," he replied. "They have some cassiterite back in the mountains, and they get copper there too, or buy it from the Carthaginians at Onuba."

He reminded me what Jason had told of Himilco's voyage for cassiterite, which got no farther than Artabria. Melting copper and cassiterite together for bronze seemed known far from Our Sea. Whether the people here learned it from the Greeks, Carthaginians, or Phoenicians, or came upon it themselves, no one could tell me. I suspected some of both.

The gaulos floated evenly on the high tide, but deeply, with water getting through the temporary covering and stuffing. When the tide fell, the gaulos eased back over to uncover the damaged area again. The time available before the next flood ran past sunset, and the men worked rapidly to fit and fasten new planks, smooth them with flat stones, and calk the new seams with papyrus tow. Leonidas again heated pitch, and by starlight and torches the men sealed the calking. The hold was bailed dry and when the tide rose again, the gaulos floated high.

Jason and Typhis went below to see–to feel in the dark–if the new work were tight. They came up satisfied for the moment.

"We will know in the morning," Jason said. "The new wood will swell. That ought to stop seepage. If not, we do it over."

Morning found the patch tight and almost dry. The lead sheathing was pounded back in place and fastened. Everything ashore was stowed. Pallets and sheepskin were hung on bushes to dry. The sails were laced to the yards. We were ready for sea.

But not to go. The Alione's ship had been rowed out in the night calm, but morning had brought a strong breeze blowing into our harbor. As Pasias had said, we could only wait. "I have spent weeks in places like this," Jason warned.

Girondas and I took my gnomon to a high level spot before noon for readings. Again, the boy Eban joined us. I looked across the broad bay outside our cove to the far shore in the bright sunlight. I saw again the tower we had passed. It looked about two hundred cubits high.

"A landmark for sailors," Girondas said. "It has been there as long as I can remember. Who built it I do not know. They say it is the work of a god. That winding ramp to the top tests a strong heart."

"What do they call it?" I asked.

"I never heard a name. Just the tower. They light a fire at the top at night if they know ships are out there. Fishermen or distant sailors like the Aliones."

"I am going to call it the Tower of Herakles, for our hero. If people here do have a name for it, it must be for someone like Herakles."

My calculations showed this harbor almost in the same latitude as Massalia, as I thought from Girondas' chart. Again, I wished for a way to count the stadia between me and home, between me and my Anticlea and Dryas and Anthia. I felt that at Massalia the sun must be at least an hour farther along. That would be an angular distance of fifteen degrees . . . but how many stadia made a degree this far from the equator?

Then I remembered the predicted conjunction of Ares and Selene the moon. I again counted back the days to equinox and realized that unless I had missed a day or two, tonight should be the night. I was grateful for the gale.

We returned to the gaulos and found Jason grumbling. "Another day lost," he said, looking at the whitecaps outside the harbor and feeling the surge from the ocean swells. He did not rejoice when I told him the delay might be profitable, but he did see the gain in possibly learning how to calculate east-west distance, in degrees at least.

"But how often does this happen?" he asked.

"Not often," was all I could tell him.

Girondas and I carefully filled the water-clock and started it at sunset. Eban brought fresh water from ashore so we would have no salt deposits inside. We also started the hourglass.

When the darkening clear sky showed the half moon, we could see red Ares close. I felt excited and I guess Girondas did too. Jason, Typhis, and Eban watched closely. Herakles watched for a while from his pallet, but soon he was asleep. It had been a day of waiting, but he had used his great muscles. He swam and ran on the beach, and he had been seen talking to a woman. He was tired.

Ares and the moon seemed stuck apart. After two hours, though, we could see the sky between getting narrower. In two more, with the hourglass turned faithfully by Eban and the water-clock dripping away, the moment was close.

Finally Ares and the moon kissed. Ares quickly went behind. We noted the level of the water-clock and turned the hourglass on its side. It was nearly five hours after sunset. I hoped some friend in Massalia had done as well.

But we still would not know how many stadia! Some day a mathematician or an astronomer will find a way to measure Earth's circumference and then we can start to work this out. We will still need to tell time to the second – none of those variable hours the Babylonians and Egyptians and even Greeks have used! – and to know the time at the same instant at Massalia, Athens, Alexandria, or wherever we put our base north-south line. I may live to see it, or my Dryas. He might even be the mathematician, although now he thinks only of the next Olympic Games.

X

THE OESTRYMNIAN GULF

AFTER TWO MORE DAYS, the aparctias gale blew itself out. There was still a westerly breeze into the bay, but we rowed far enough out of the cove to sail. We angled this way and that across the wind in short runs until we had a clear way north.

Again I watched with admiration Jason's men working together on quick changes in course. Jason had only to call that he was going to cross the wind. Typhis swung the steering oar easily, the men quickly released lines, hauled the sails, the main again a brailed triangle, to the other side, and secured them again. Typhis changed oars and the gaulos made smooth arcs. Herakles and Girondas watched for shoals or rocks from the prow.

When we settled northerly, I saw we had some distance before turning east into the Oestrymnian Gulf. Soon we eased to northeasterly, and the gaulos boiled through the water. Dolphins played as in Our Sea and the white-capped waves glittered. It was a day to enjoy. Greeks have always loved dolphins.

"We should have more days like this," I told Jason.

"Have your fun while you can," he replied. "This gulf can give trouble."

Before long we rounded another great headland, crossed the mouth of

---

The gaulos rounds Spain's Cabo Ortegal and heads east. A threatening electrical storm drives them into the harbor at Guetaria, behind San Antón, an island called The Mouse. (Guetaria was to become, in 1476 or 1487, the birthplace of Juan Sebastián Delcano, who finished the slain Ferdinand Magellan's voyage around the world in 1522). The gaulos goes into the Gironde River with its tidal bore, passes the mouth of the Liger (Loire), and a gale drives it into the Baie de Quiberon and to the coast of Morbihan, where they see Locmariaquer's Grand Menhir, now lying broken on the ground, and the complex of standing stones nearby.

another large inlet, and began a long easterly course. We kept the rugged shoreline in sight, and Jason watched the skies.

"Fair weather clouds." He pointed to the scattered, billowy clouds drifting from the west. "May they stay with us." Jason spent as much time watching skies as sea. He seemed uneasy. I asked if he were worried.

"Just trying not to be surprised."

"I haven't seen you surprised yet, even by the Maurusians."

But he was surprised, in the best way, by continuing good weather. We sailed easily and fast, with little change in our now square mainsail and artemon. The wind stayed behind, almost as if ordered. Even so, after a few days, when the sky seemed most brilliant, Jason kept watching haze along the western horizon.

"Some change making up," he said. "We better get in." That was midmorning. The haze spread slowly but with little other change. Still Jason watched it and the rocky coastline. Girondas watched too and I heard him say, "Unless I have forgotten more than I think, we should find a good harbor in an hour or so."

"If the wind holds," Jason said.

"If the wind quits, we'd better get the oars out and head offshore fast," Girondas added. "I think we have a few hours."

In late afternoon, we saw ahead a rounded knob that seemed part of the coast.

"That's it," Girondas said. "That's the island that looks like a whale. People here call it 'The Mouse.' Behind it is a snug hole."

Jason looked back at the haze. The sun, dropping toward its setting, was dimming. I thought there should have been a black cloud-line to mark a storm, but Jason said, "Not always. Not yet anyway. This will hit tonight, I think."

We saw other boats heading in. "They know, all right," Girondas said. "The harbor will be crowded. This is the only good one for a long way."

The knob became a whale-shaped island. With the threat behind us, and despite Jason's assurance that the storm would not hit until night, I felt anxious now. As well as we were sailing, it seemed an endless wait to come up to the island and harbor entrance.

"It always seems that way," Jason laughed. "Your philosophers can explain."

"They confuse more than they explain," I told him. "Right now most of them in Athens act as if mathematics were a religion and they were

A stone anchor used by Mediterranean ships in the fourth century B.C.

priests, and mere astronomers and geographers shouldn't be allowed to use it."

"Or sailors," Jason added.

We swung behind the island. It now looked much like a gigantic whale, several stadia long, capped with trees but with jagged rocks for shores, here and there a small beach. Small fishing boats already were being hauled up on bayside beaches of the island, and along mainland and creek shores. Larger ones, which Girondas said hunted whales offshore, came in, also to be beached and tied to trees. Still larger ones went to quays and we could see their crews setting extra lines.

Typhis, with Girondas, Jason, and Herakles watching the water, steered to a protected spot. With oars, half the crew stopped the boat. Others dropped the furled sails and yards to the deck and lashed them to stanchions. Jason and others lowered our heaviest lead anchor in water about ten cubits deep. Jason then had the oarsmen back hard. The anchor dragged. The men raised it part way.

Jason waved the gaulos fifty cubits forward and the anchor was dropped again. It held. "I hope we can get it up."

The oarsmen and Typhis then moved us forward at an angle of almost ninety degrees. A second anchor was dropped when Jason called the spot. We again backed away hard. It held. The two lines then were let out a long distance, with some kept tightly coiled on deck.

"Why so much line?" I asked. "Won't we swing farther in the wind?"

"Better swing than drag. The more line, the less upward pull."

He shortened up when other boats our size came looking for anchorages. "They would make room for me," Jason said.

Dusk fell but the storm had not yet hit. Girondas thought we had an hour or two after we had lashed everything on deck tightly. The last rays of sunshine turned the high tips of a growing mass of clouds gold and pink. The wind became a fitful breeze.

"Let's go ashore and see what food we can buy," Jason said to Leonidas. "We have plenty, but now we turn north toward Armorica and the Veneti are not so friendly. Besides we will all feel better with something fresh." We had had nothing fresh since finishing the goat from the Urium.

I gave him a gold stater, which is accepted everywhere in Iberia, and they went in our small boat. Girondas stayed aboard.

"Tomorrow, if this blows over, I will see if I can find anybody I know," he said.

"Who are these people?" I asked.

"This is the country of the Aliones," he replied. "They are not Keltoi. Jason and I know enough to talk with them. Many here go after whales. They go out in small boats and drive spears into the whales, some bigger than this gaulos. Others fish for herring, tunny, eels, and lobsters. Still others voyage far, like the captain we talked to the other day. It is a hard life and many die, but these people live their own lives and know no master."

"What do they eat?" I asked. I could see sheep on the hills, but there seemed to be little level space for farming or even small gardens, and no olive groves.

"They do not grow olives. You have to like whale oil here."

Jason and Leonidas returned after dark with sacks of beans and grain and a goat-skin of wine. "That is rugged, red wine," Girondas warned me. "Let the men have it. It will not last. Be glad!"

Jason was somber. "They think this is going to be a bad one," he said. "We will see before long."

Thunder rumbled to the west, and Jason made a last deck inspection. The air was still and sticky, the night hot. The slightest effort put me in a sweat. We all waited on deck. We watched stragglers come in and head for the beaches.

"Waiting is as bad as having it," I complained.

"It will be worse than you think," Jason warned.

Indeed, it was.

It was a mighty storm, possibly two or three colliding over us. For three or more hours great thunderbolts struck about the hills and villages, with quick, deafening roars. Gusts stronger than I had ever felt whipped our gaulos and other anchored boats about. The gusts came from everywhere, and when one hit a boat broadside, it heeled over with a snap. Several capsized. We heeled enough several times to put water half across the deck. The men had to scramble to balance, then rush back for the next gust from the other side.

Only a tremendous rain kept the harbor smooth. Water cascaded down slopes ashore, washing mud out to turn the harbor opaque—when thunderbolts showed it to us.

Several beached boats were washed back into the bay by a rush of water down a creek. They drifted about, hitting anchored craft and finally swamping. We saw at least one bigger boat break free, to be blown out to sea.

Jason kept our oars manned, and often had the men row to ease the anchor lines. It was frightening to do this with bolts striking all around. I expected to see our mast, higher than anything near us, struck.

The cold rain and little round white stones from the sky beat on us, already chilled by the wind. Jason kept everybody on deck so no one could be trapped if we capsized, also to fend off drifting boats and debris. Herakles was called upon several times to push something heavy away. Once he had to swing out on an anchor line like an ape to clear a snagged tree trunk. For all his size, he came back hand over hand. The gaulos surged forward with each swing.

We could see little. The rain was as thick as a cloud, and we had to keep our eyes closed most of the time because of its stinging force. Once in a lull I saw a fire ashore, started by a bolt. Nobody there was safer. The blaze was drowned in a few minutes, and somebody's thatched roof now had a hole with rain pouring through.

In time the storm moved on. Flashes of bolts came at longer intervals, thunder became more distant. Somebody farther east now was catching it.

But the heavy rain continued. The wind died and Jason told the rowers to bring their oars aboard and go below if they wanted shelter. He and Herakles stayed on deck, beards dripping like black sponges, and the rest of us did go to the hold, to crowd ourselves amid the stores. We all had been washed clean by the rain, but in the close heat, we soon began to sweat. Most found rain on deck better.

Jason had been busy catching drifting skiffs. Herakles had brought aboard usable timbers and a drowned ram. "It will be tough but it will give us meat," Jason said. "Also a skin."

By daybreak the rain stopped. We could see fading stars. Sun-up showed a washed world, but one of devastation where streams had flooded or where gusts had torn off roofs or pushed over small buildings. People ashore cleared wreckage and started rebuilding. Fishermen rounded up their boats, including those Jason had caught.

Jason was anxious to sail. After a quick breakfast he, Girondas, and I went ashore to see if we could add anything to our stores. Leonidas dressed the ram.

Girondas and I searched quays and streets to ask for older men who might remember him. People who could take a few seconds from repair work could tell us little.

"The men I knew are mostly dead," he sighed at last. "It has been ten years or more. One still alive is at sea and no one knows when he will come home."

"Does anyone know about lands to the north?" I asked.

"If they do, they do not tell me. We cannot expect too much. They are townsmen and men who fish nearby, not sailors. Distant sailors are all at sea. Some of these are shipbuilders, but shipbuilders are not sailors. They have heard of Albion and Ierné and even Samland, but they have never been far from here."

Jason returned with two live lambs around his neck, then went back for feed. Soon we were all aboard and ready to sail.

There was little wind, so we rowed out. Wind was no better in the gulf, and we kept rowing easily, almost north. I looked back and imagined what the rugged shores must have looked like in the storm. On the rocks we saw a few wrecked boats.

In about two hours Jason sighted a drifting boat the size of ours. Typhis circled it. "We could claim it, I guess," Jason said, "but somebody back there needs it." He sent Herakles to drop its anchor.

"Now we head again for your Hyperborean lands," Jason said. "We want to keep away from shore. The coast is low. I do not know it too well, but there are offshore shoals."

"I have heard there is a river somewhere north of here that rises far back inland, near where rivers flowing to Our Sea start," I said. "Can we see it? It's probably a route for cassiterite."

"I know that river. We may pass close. If the weather is good, we can go in. There is a good harbor, but there is a dangerous rock in the mouth, and a dangerous wave rushes upstream at the start of the flood tide. The people there are Keltoi, but we are getting close to the Veneti. We may not be welcome. Probably some of your cassiterite goes up. There are other rivers that go far back."

We did head in. Jason waited outside until the rising tide was an hour old. "Tides get more powerful as we go north," he said. "I do not want to ride that first wave past that big rock."

We found a quay, and Jason, Girondas, and I went ashore. As Jason had expected, the people were less friendly. We did see a few boats carrying cassiterite ingots of knucklebone shape. The ingots were being transferred to shallow river craft, apparently to be towed up by men or horses or poled by their crews.

My Keltoi was either not understood or ignored, and Jason and Girondas had little better luck. Jason did find one shipment destined for Massalia, but the man he talked to was quickly silenced by a companion.

As soon as the tide turned, Jason took us out. We had learned little, except that this was a port for transshipment despite its distance from where Girondas said the Cassiterides and Albion were. The river seemed to flow mostly from the direction of Massalia, but how far a boat could be taken no one would tell us, or how close the upper reaches came to the Rhodanus or Arar.

Outside the wind was fitful. Jason had us rowed for several hours and kept a close watch on the sky. Indeed the weather was unsettled, and we could see squalls, some with thunder and flashing bolts, scattered about the horizon. Typhis kept a steady northwestward course, getting farther from shore. "We are not in deep water," Jason explained. "It is dangerous in a storm."

In a day the wind settled northwest and pressed us inshore. The coast trended out to meet us. Sailing across the wind and back gained little, and rowing was the only way to move. We passed several islands, then had to go between one and the mainland.

"We have passed the Liger, another big river," Jason told me. "A cassiterite trading town called Corbilo is there, but we would not learn as much there as before. We are too close to the Veneti. Let's keep going."

Keeping going continued hard, and when the wind finally swung southerly, it was a gale. It drove us into a bay behind a long point stretching out westward, and we found shelter in a connecting bay. At the narrow entrance, we saw a tall tower ashore. As soon as we were secure, Girondas and I went to see it. Eban spoke to Jason and was waved on with us.

"It has been there a long time," Girondas said. "It is one huge rock cut in that shape. Nobody built it. How they got it to stand I do not know."

It stood straight and I thought at once it must be a gnomon. Perhaps there was study of geometry here too! But nobody could or would tell us. One did say that in "some forgotten time" it had been used for watching the heavens. Nearby were eleven rows of standing stones, each line about six stadia long. The whole had to be some astronomical or mathematical tool!

I had brought my cross-staff, but the people would not let me take a sight of the tip. They made it plain with gestures that the cross-staff must be an evil device! The best I could do was a silent estimate of the height at fifty cubits. I gave one man a small bronze bangle. He took it but just shook his head at Girondas' questions in Keltoi. Even if he understood, he did not know who were were or what we wanted, and probably did not want to. Eban tried to pace off the sun's shadow but was stopped.

"It will be like that all along," Jason said when we returned. "The Veneti are suspicious of any stranger."

"So are we," I said. "Even our best Massaliots call all non-Greeks barbarians."

"You think about it – the Veneti are like Carthaginians. They control shipping here as Carthage does our western waters."

I asked if they were as rich and powerful. Jason agreed they must be rich, with their fine oaken ships and leather-covered craft that brought so much to them. "Powerful enough to scare off anybody else wanting to get cassiterite and elektron."

"Do they have any beautiful city like Carthage?" I asked.

Neither Jason nor Girondas knew. I kept my curiosity in check. We might have to deal with Veneti traders, but I wanted no spear in my back. In most societies a scientist was safe, but the Veneti were an unknown. If we found their Carthage, we might not leave alive!

We sailed again as soon as the gale eased. As the gaulos was rowed past the tower, I took an angle with my cross-staff and estimated the distance to the base. I came close to confirming my fifty-cubit guess for the height.

"I have also heard that there are others like that, not so high, marking trading routes across the land," Girondas said, "and in Albion there are supposed to be strange arrays of many stones, some with others laid across the top."

"What are they for?" I asked.

"I only know what I have heard. They may be for watching the heavens, or for some worship rituals, or both. One man told me that you could stand at one stone at solstice and sight the sun rising over another, and that risings and settings of the moon could be sighted on lines of other stones at different times. Eclipses of the moon could be foretold, he claimed. But the ones I have heard about are all inland and I never got to see them. The Carthaginians had no interest with rich trade not a likelihood."

Something more to think about. ". . . They may be for watching the heavens . . ." When we got to Albion, I would try to see these stones.

XI

ON A ROCKY ISLET

I TOLD JASON ABOUT my new interest as we headed on. The coast curved northwest and a continuing southerly breeze helped us toward a big island he called Uexisamé.

"I would like to see those stones, too," Jason said. "But you want to get as far north as we can for solstice, and we have only about six weeks."

"I should be a dozen men in a dozen boats," I sighed.

We stopped at the big island. Jason watched tidal stages closely. The men had to row strongly across tidal streams to get us into a quiet cove. Rough, irregular seas fell over each other to jolt the gaulos and make rowing difficult. Girondas and I went ashore just before noon, joined again by young Eban, with my gnomon. Eban watched closely. Jason had urged him to learn all he could. "Some day you may have a ship."

Eban soon had a starting grasp of mathematics from me and of its use in navigation from Girondas and Jason. As a practical help, he could carry the gnomon. Some climbs up rugged shores made extra–and younger–muscles helpful.

We found a level spot and got our noon sun reading. We looked to the east and could just see the mainland, Calbron, about one hundred and fifty stadia away. To the west was Okeanos, again stretching far beyond

---

Girondas mentions Belerion (southwestern England) and the Cassiterides, the "Tin Islands" thought then to be the Scillies, and describes the English Channel or La Manche, with the North Sea beyond. The gaulos crosses the Golfe de Saint-Malo, with Pytheas watching Arktos (the Great Bear or Big Dipper). Jason warns of rocky dangers, including Les Minquiers and the Oestrymnides (Channel Islands). They pass the Casquets and the tide forces them to an anchorage in a cove of a rocky islet between the Casquets and Alderney where they rescue a shipwrecked party from Albion. They go on to make port among Veneti on the Sequana River (the Seine) after waiting out its great tidal bore. Pytheas asks for information about the Gulf of Metuonis (the Baltic Sea) and its amber.

any horizon, perhaps to India, perhaps to that land the Alione told of. From his description, as vague as he kept it, that land must extend much farther north.

Eban listened closely as Girondas told what he knew. The boy was picking up the Greek Girondas used in speaking to me, and Girondas put back into Tartessan enough for Eban to follow.

"I have stopped here," Girondas said, "usually on the way to Ierné for gold. Pritania's or Albion's Belerion, with the tip that ends in the islands you Greeks call the Cassiterides, is due north, about two days' sail. Then Pritania and this eastern mainland curve, almost parallel, to the east. This strait lies between. It gets narrower until it is only about three hundred stadia from shore to shore. There it ends. This mainland coast goes on curving northeastward, and Pritania's turns north, with a widening sea and a rough one between."

"The Carthaginians went these ways?" I asked.

"No, I never got to see what I now tell you. But I heard it from sailors, even Veneti when they had enough wine, but mostly from others from the mainland and from another land on to the north. They come down this way to trade and they too are great sailors. They have to be, for their own land is bounded on the west by much rough water beating on their rocky shores and into their deep inlets between mountains."

We returned to the gaulos. We had carefully tied our small boat to a tree but found that the ebbing tide had left it half a stadium from the water. We had to drag it through mud to launch.

We had seen no one, although there were paths around the cove. A few rough buildings were perhaps for trading. This thought was strengthened when we saw that a strange boat had sailed into the cove, to investigate us or on business of its own.

It was round, with no oarsmen to move it if the wind died. It seemed to be built of a light frame with something stretched over. The men aboard watched but did not speak to us.

"Veneti with one of their leather boats," Jason said. He hailed them in Keltoi. One waved but no one called back.

"Show them something bright," Jason said to me. I held a trifle above my head. The man beckoned to us. We rowed alongside. I showed him the trinket, an elektron center in a bronze ring, with a bronze chain, all polished.

"Ask him what he will trade," I said. The man shook his head. Jason

An Eskimo skin boat, similar in construction to the Veneti ship.

pointed to a mat covering cargo, but the man said nothing. I did see and admire the way cowhides were stitched together for a water-tight hull, with others for the sail. I wondered about such boats in a storm.

We waved and rowed to sea. The Veneti watched us, without hostility, without friendship.

"He had cassiterite or raw elektron," Jason said.

Jason headed us northeast. The wind was southwest, not strong but raising a steep, choppy sea. "Why is the sea so rough?" I asked. Jason told me of the strong tidal currents. "When the wind is against them, the chop is worse."

He said we would pass more islands, the Oestrymnides, and rocks that showed and disappeared with the tides as soon as we crossed a wide bay; then we would head on for the narrowest part of the strait and probably cross to Kantion on Pritania. "All dangerous water. Rough. Storms. Heavy fogs. You see nothing then."

I had found Uexisamé at close to fifty degrees, nearly seven north of Massalia. Eban tried his hand and came near my figure. All he needed was practice.

The southwest breeze held and we made good time. The land to the east edged away and during the night we were alone on open ocean again, Arktos wheeling around our guide stars. "Open but shallow," Jason said. "Be glad we have no gale."

I talked more to Girondas. Again and again I was glad he had walked those weary stadia from Illipla. I felt that Jason was as glad. Girondas knew what might take us many days to learn.

"Albion or Pritania," I asked, "is it a land mass like Keltika?"

"I do not think so. I think it is a big island, bigger than any other in Okeanos that we know of."

Jason gave the steering oar to Typhis and joined us. He was now close to the far end of his own knowledge.

Girondas told what he had heard from other sailors, of trading ships from the Hyperborean lands sailing down the western side of Pritania, to reach Belerion that way, or to go to Ierné.

"Ierné is said to be another big island. Some of those Hyperborean traders even have had to come down its western coast, on Okeanos. It is not so big as Pritania, but still bigger than anything we know from Phoenicia to the Pillars of Herakles, bigger than that Minoan island that also grew such great sailors before our time. A sea almost as rough as this strait runs between Ierné and Pritania. Again I always wanted to see for myself, but Carthaginians are never explorers. Some elektron traders go that way to Belerion to trade with Veneti getting cassiterite."

As we crossed the wide bay, Jason, Herakles, Girondas, and the others kept a close lookout after dawn. "These islands have wrecked many ships," Jason said. "Some east of here are surrounded by stadium after stadium of rocks, reefs, and shoals that appear and disappear with tides ranging twenty or more cubits. You think you are floating fine at high tide, and find yourself in the air at low."

"I hope you know where they are," I said.

"I kept far enough away," Jason replied.

In time we sighted an island and headed more northerly. Jason said another lay about two hundred stadia southeast, but we did not see it in haze.

"On ahead a little way are the worst of all," Jason added. "A chain sticking out nearly two hundred stadia from a headland. Terrible tidal currents through islands and rocks. Different every tide, every hour of every tide. Many rocks under water all the time, others at high tide. One big island, the rest little. No place to get caught out in fog or storm."

Jason and Typhis kept well away and we passed the outermost islets and headed east, ten stadia or more off the chain. We could see the islets, but few rocks. "Tide is too high," Jason said.

The tide starting to ebb rushed through the islets and the men had to row in bad chop and overfalls to help the sail. We found ourselves quartering more to the north to keep from being swept on rocks. The tiring men sweated in the warm air but had to keep pulling. We made little progress. Jason saw a small cove on an islet east of the westernmost rock group and headed us in to wait for the tide to turn fair. An upright stone, like the one we had seen in our storm haven but much shorter, stood on a cliff.

As we came in, weaving deftly around rocks, we saw two small figures on the shore, waving, beckoning to us. "Looks like a trap," Jason warned. "People wreck ships for loot."

"They're children," I protested.

"With fathers and uncles behind rocks."

Girondas thought not. Jason reluctantly let him, Eban, and me row ashore. Eban stayed with the skiff to move it with falling tide. Jason kept the anchor hove short – for quick flight.

The boy was a child, the small, yellow-haired girl a few years older than Eban. They seemed almost as wary of us as Jason of them. But they were formal, the boy even bowed. Their torn robes were of good wool and linen. They were no savages.

Then the girl spoke urgently and pointed back among the rocks. "My father!" she said in a Keltoi I could follow. I sensed that he needed help quickly. Girondas confirmed this. "They are wrecked here," he said.

She led us through the rocks. Behind a huge boulder we found a torn skin boat, a dying man lying on the folded leather sail in a nearby cave mouth, and a tall, middle-aged woman. The girl knelt beside him.

He saw me and closed his eyes, trying to speak. His whispers were agonized. I think his back had been broken. There was nothing we could do, not even Girondas, so capable in so many things. The man died as we tried to ease his pain.

Then a strange ceremony took place. The tall woman knelt before the girl. The boy did likewise. The woman removed a gold neckpiece from the man and handed it to the boy. The girl knelt and he placed it around her throat.

She and the woman gently took off the dead man's wide belt, studded with gold and bronze, and put it on the boy. Asking the girl's permission, the woman took silver jewels from the body and hid them under her cloak. The girl covered her neckpiece with her own. The boy covered his belt.

"My father was a king," the girl sobbed. "He must be buried like a king–not here with stones, but at sea. Please, for us!"

Girondas talked with her more easily than I could as she and the boy and the woman cut leather from the broken boat-frame with her father's big knife and wrapped the body. Girondas rolled up the leather sail.

We carried the body to the skiff. Eban rowed it out, then returned for us.

Jason was disturbed. "Who are they?" he demanded. "What we are getting into?"

"They are not of the people who live on these islands," Girondas reassured him. "Those people do wreck boats. I feel she speaks truth. She says he was a great man somewhere in Albion. They were being pursued and were wrecked in a storm. They lived in the cave more than a week. At least we can bury him as she asks."

"But women!" Jason said angrily. "Women are bad on a ship."

"We can land them on Kantion," Girondas said.

As upset as he was, Jason would not have left them on the islet, I felt sure. He continued to grumble, but when the tide turned we made out to sea and as soon as we were far enough, he stopped the ship and had ballast stones placed with the wrapped body. The woman, the girl, and the boy struggled to lift it. Jason signed to Herakles, and the giant gently raised it to the rail. He stepped back and the three eased it into the water. It sank quickly. They watched the bubbles rise.

Then the woman turned to us. Her eyes were red but dry. The girl wept, but with composure. The boy was wide-eyed, partly with grief, partly with curiosity. What world were we from?

"You have done more than you know," the woman said. "Our gods will reward you."

"Perhaps your gods joined ours to send us to you," Girondas replied. "Now, tell us who you are."

She put her arm around the girl and said, "Princess . . . Queen Tregela." The girl seemed startled. The woman laid her hand on the boy's head and said, "Prince Rob." She pointed to herself. "I am Barda. The king was my brother. Our kingdom is in the land of the Durotriges in Albion."

Jason was standing by, his face still grim. Her native language seemed other than Keltoi and she had to pick her words carefully but both Jason and I could follow her. "We will pay you for our passage," she continued, holding out a piece of gold. Jason turned away.

"We will take you where we go and land you in Pritania where we can," he said. "We have our own way to go."

Barda started to plead, but said nothing when Girondas motioned to her. We saw Jason talking to Leonidas, and Leonidas came to them and said, "I will try to make you comfortable. We have little room."

The gaulos was sailing easily to the east, twenty or so stadia off the mainland. The men kept busy, with many glances at our new passengers, mostly the little queen. The younger sailors tried to make themselves neater. The girl herself wrapped her hair around her head and pulled her hood close, and looked more like a boy.

Girondas and Leonidas lashed the wreck's leather sail to rails and stanchions for a tent-like shelter in the point of the foredeck. They lashed a wide earthen jar to the stem. They placed the skiff across the shelter opening for privacy.

"Have you eaten?" Leonidas asked. Barda told him they had been on the islet a week, eating food from the wrecked boat, a seabird Rob had caught, and oysters and mussels pried from rocks at low tide. They had rain water and dew to drink.

Leonidas brought them cold food left from our last meal, and also found straw and old sails for pallets. Tregela the queen, exhausted emotionally and physically, soon was asleep. Prince Rob sat on the skiff watching everything. Barda stood at the rail, looking across the water toward Albion.

I asked Jason where we were going next and he replied, a little more loudly than usual, "Into a Veneti port where you can learn more. The Sequana. Lots of shipping there. They won't tell you anything but you can see."

A Celtic royal neckpiece such as that placed on Tregela's neck after her father's death.

Barda must have heard him. She came aft and said, "Please, not the Sequana."

Jason ignored her. I had never seen him so rude. Nor had he mentioned the Sequana before and I had thought we would go to Albion, even though we were headed another direction. "You want to see the cassiterite and elektron trading, don't you?" he asked me. "And we need stores if we are to have these people with us."

Girondas reminded him of a tidal wave there much worse than at the first river we entered. Jason argued that the Veneti went in and out as they pleased, but Girondas said that they were about the only ones who knew how.

"We'll row in on the ebb if we have to."

"You can't fight all that water coming out." Girondas said no more. Jason's temper had not eased.

But we did wait outside until we could see the water line creeping up the beaches, between marks that showed ten to fifteen cubits range between low and high water. The sails were furled and the men rowed carefully. Girondas and Jason at our prow signaled Typhis around bars and snags. We rode the crest of a late wave, perhaps a cubit high, and Girondas piloted us into a cove busy with other craft.

Barda, Tregela, and Rob went under their shelter. I could hear Barda apparently telling the boy to keep out of sight. There was something here she feared.

Trading ship from Norway moored near the gaulos.

"Only that the Veneti go to Belerion for it."

"Did you find out how to get to Abalus?" Jason asked. "I heard you ask but couldn't get what he said."

"Keep going, north and east," Girondas replied. "There is a helpful current along the eastern side of that sea beyond the strait much of the time. It is shallow and he says a ship can go aground far offshore. Much of the land is so low that storms flood it for many stadia inland. There is a chain of low islands along the shore. But in time you come to Abalus, which is a big island. Just beyond its tip is the entrance to a large gulf with no tides. There are many small islands in that entrance."

"Did he say anything about the river Tanaïs?" I asked. "It is supposed to flow into that Gulf of Metuonis and some say it also flows into our Euxine Sea."

"That must be in Samland, the Balt country to the east. He said he did not sail there and knew little about it. That Tanaïs must be two rivers that start close together somewhere far south."

More for my journal. Meanwhile, we lay on deck to sleep. Jason told Eban to stand anchor watch, either for intruders or for our men. The boy was delighted. If he knew that Jason would awaken at any strange sound, still not a fish jumped without his attention.

Before I fell asleep, I heard Barda and Tregela stirring. They talked in low tones. Barda seemed to be trying to comfort and reassure the girl. Barda came out of the shelter and looked around in the dark, then went back in. The girl came out to stretch and breathe deeply, then returned. The young prince slept as a healthy boy should.

As Jason knew, the men came back as eastern stars began to fade. They tried to be quiet, but they had had a good time.

Herakles carried two, dipped them head first in the water, and soon all were ready to pick up oars. I knew how sailors behaved at Massalia, but Jason explained that rigid life under Carthaginians carried over here.

I could have wished to feel as good. As little of the Abalans' drink as I had taken, I had a headache and sour taste.

Jason laughed. "Next time, pour that brown stuff on the ground when no one is looking."

This was small comfort, but my headache wore off with the ebb tide. We had heard the roar of big waves going by out in the river when the flood started, and we knew we had hours to wait. The gaulos rose and dipped in the backwash.

We saw the big man return to his leather boat with his servant. He looked at us sharply. After raising anchor, he brought his boat close but sailed by without speaking. "No Veneti," Girondas said.

After the boat was far enough away, Barda called. Girondas went forward and sat on the skiff, facing aft. He listened, then returned.

"She watched him through the hawsehole," he told us. "He wants to kill them and be king of their land, she says."

XII

THROUGH THE FOG

IN OPEN SEA Jason headed northeast, for Kantion and the narrow strait. Again it was either sailing to a cassiterite port of Belerion, or racing the solstice. "Belerion later," Jason said. "We'll land these people on Kantion." We had seen the leather boat in another cove.

The southwesterly breeze kept us moving. Jason often noted tidal currents slowing us, then helping. We had mostly good weather, but toward the end of the third day we were heading, and rapidly in a rising wind, into one of those clouds of fog. Jason had said we would see almost nothing, and he was right.

"What makes it sit upon the sea?" I asked. "It doesn't even blow away in a wind."

"All I know is that this strait is this way too much."

We were deep in it. In rifts we could see scarcely half a stadium, most of the time barely our prow.

He had Girondas and Herakles on lookout at the prow, Eban and Leonidas on either side. Typhis steered and Jason watched our wake. If it strayed from straight, he called a correction. The only other sounds were of rushing water, wind, and a howl from Herakles every minute or so. He had powerful lungs.

"If anybody is close, maybe he will hear," Jason said. "If we are lucky."

The wind strengthened and Jason ordered the sails down. "Going too fast. This would be fine if we could just see." The bare mast was enough

---

The gaulos heads farther into the English Channel, and another rescue is undertaken. They finally make harbor in a creek entering Kent's Pegwell Bay, near Ramsgate. The rescued sailor, Simon, describes his home port at Boulby Head, far on to the north and the highest headland on England's North Sea coast. He pilots them past the Goodwin Sands at the mouth of the Tamesis (the Thames River).

sail, for we kept moving so Typhis could steer. The motion of the boat was easier, too, for the sea was rough in what was now nearly a gale. We took much spray aboard, and it was cold. Girondas wrapped himself in his sheepskin, and Jason gave Typhis the skin off the drowned Iberian ram. The rest of us got wet. I was miserable. Leonidas passed out bread and cheese for supper. Wine would have been welcome, but Leonidas dared not pour. Anyway, a cup of wine would have been soon salted.

Jason had Leonidas move our passengers into the hold and take down their shelter before it blew away.

For hours we sailed on. Jason was worried. "We could be heading straight for rocks." He called Girondas aft. Girondas too had seen less of these waters than he wished, but he felt we were safe. "You can't be sure with all the commotion," he said, "but the wind does seem steady and straight. Maybe some day somebody will make something to tell us our heading at any time. Put your son to it, Pytheas."

Hour after dark, anxious hour passed. Jason relieved Typhis but took no rest himself. Typhis dozed in a sheltered corner, as did the others. Herakles stayed at the prow alone, for Girondas too had to rest. Leonidas reported our passengers sick and miserable.

All we could do was steer and watch. There were no sails. Nor was there water in the hold or shifting of ballast or cargo. When Herakles' mighty voice became hoarse, Eban asked to take over lookout. "Go ahead," Jason told him, "but hold on. A man overboard is hard enough to see in calm sunlight."

The boy crawled forward. Herakles looked doubtful and stayed long enough to be sure Eban was safe. Even with the boy holding a stanchion and rigging, Herakles passed a rope around him.

Eban's voice did not match Herakles' but carried well. He had been there an hour when he shouted back and pointed ahead. Jason rushed forward. I held the steering oar until Typhis could take it.

Jason signaled Typhis to sheer away from something Eban had sighted in a rift.

It was an overturned boat, about the size of ours. An exhausted man clung to it, his head just above the cold water.

Jason ordered four men to back oars. We eased to the hulk, just keeping the oars clear. Herakles threw a coiled line. The wind carried the end away. Jason put two more men to oars and stopped us. Typhis played the steering oar to stay upwind. Herakles tried again from the prow. The rope landed close, but the man was too weak. The end soon flew away again.

Jason brought the gaulos even closer, until our heaving prow was within two or three cubits. The men rowed and backed skillfully in the turmoil.

Herakles let himself down on a rope and in a few seconds could step on the heaving hulk. Jason backed us away quickly. Herakles, trailing a lifeline, spread himself across the hulk, wriggled close, reached down, grabbed the man's arm, and pulled him up.

The unstable hulk rolled, and Herakles and the barely conscious man both slid off. Jason and Typhis by now had laid the gaulos athwart the hulk for a little protection. Half our men stood with poles to fend off. I took a pole and stood with them.

Jason went to the rail and pulled in Herakles' line. Herakles held the man with one arm, the rope with the other hand. He knotted the rope around the man's chest. Jason and Eban hoisted him aboard. Herakles held to the end of an oar, the oarsman deftly raising and lowering it with the waves. Then Jason dropped the rope to him. He made himself fast and waved to Jason to get the gaulos clear.

Jason ordered our wildly rolling ship forward. Typhis brought the prow to the wind as soon as we were clear. Herakles was towed along, battered against the side.

We now pitched as wildly as we had rolled. Jason ordered half the oars stowed and the men went to pull up Herakles. But just as Herakles reached to grab the rail, the rope broke. He dropped into the waves.

I was closest and he seized the end of my pole. Jason and three men rushed to help hold it. Others got a heavier rope, quickly knotted a loop, and let it down.

Herakles was hauled aboard. On deck even he lay and panted. This was no warm summer water of Our Sea. Girondas and Typhis threw their sheepskins over him. Then we thought – what of the rescued man? Could he be alive?

He was, not by much. He still lay on the foredeck. He breathed, but he had been long in the cold water. During a lull, Leonidas and I got him to a pallet in the hold and covered him. Leonidas dipped a cup of wine, I held the man's head up, and helped him sip. We rubbed his arms and legs.

Barda crawled from her cramped spot. "This is for women," she told us. "You are needed up there."

We came up while Barda and Tregela, forgetting their own miseries, nursed the man.

"They are some use after all," Jason said.

We drifted backwards, our prow to the wind, Jason and Typhis fighting both steering oars. Jason shouted for all oars. He watched the steep waves – the wind must be against the tide – for long minutes. He shouted again when he saw his chance.

The men on the right pulled, those on the left backed. The gaulos spun in a trough wider than most. We again "sailed" downwind.

I looked back. The hulk was lost in fog and spray. Then Jason and I saw it rise close astern on a crest higher than our mast, and up-end. When we rose, only foam was there.

We were alone with our own problems. The gale and fog continued. The oars were stowed. Jason again streamed all heavy ropes astern, although the foul tidal current must have slowed us even more. He and Typhis brought the steering oars aboard. We drifted.

It was hard to tell when dawn came. Leonidas passed up more bread and cheese. He reported the rescued man still alive, with the women doing all they could. The seas grew higher and more confused. "We must be close to the narrowest part," Jason said.

But as he had told me in our first storm, "Any weather ends." In midmorning the great fog cleared and the sun came out. The gale moderated. The seas were still high, but less powerful. Jason first put up our little storm sail and hauled in the trailing ropes, and an hour later raised our mainsail, then the artemon. Typhis could steer, even with waves coming astern trying to throw us sideways. Herakles, as strong as ever, helped.

"Where are we?" I asked. "Does anybody know?"

"I think off Kantion," Jason replied. "If you see white cliffs, shout." He waved to the left.

About noon I did see the glint of sun from those cliffs. Girondas said, "Kantion." He soon recognized marks he had not seen for ten or more years.

"There should be a bay there with a creek," he said after a while. "Head in close. Slowly, slowly – shoals."

We found the harbor, but with the tide ebbing, the creek seemed to be narrowing rapidly. Girondas at the prow signaled us past sandbars, snags, and rocks. We saw boats lying on now dry shores. Some were propped on stilts, some sitting on their bottoms, upright or careened. Men on shore watched us, we hoped only with curiosity.

Girondas brought us to a spot with water looking deep enough to float us no matter how low the tide. We anchored and Jason, Typhis, and Girondas relaxed at last.

"No more of that, ever," Jason sighed. "I hope."

Girondas laughed wearily. "This coast is famous for it."

"How is our new man?" Jason asked Leonidas.

"He will live. He has eaten a little and had some wine. The women did well with him. He can come up into the sunshine."

"Who is he?"

"I do not understand all he tries to tell me. I think he is from north of here."

As we spoke, the man's head appeared in the hatch. The man, who seemed about middle-aged, crawled weakly on deck and looked gratefully about. Herakles put him gently on his feet. He stood swaying. Herakles steadied him. His eyes sought Leonidas, the first he had seen on regaining consciousness, and he reached to him. Leonidas pointed to Herakles, then to Jason and Eban.

"They saved you," Leonidas said in Keltoi.

Jason had him sit on deck. We gathered around. Jason and Girondas tried Keltoi dialects, gestures, and signs. Slowly they got to understand each other. Barda, who had followed to the deck with Tregela and Rob, often helped. Jason glowered at first, then listened to her. I hoped his resentment was tempering. Some women may be, as he said, "bad on a ship," but not these.

The man's name was something like Simonides, the name of Jason's Samian ancestor. We called him Simon.

He lived far north on Pritania. He said his home port was marked by the highest headland and looked out on that stormy sea between Pritania and the mainland. Girondas judged it about opposite Abalus. "In the land of the Picts," he said.

Simon was a sailor on a small ship trading wool and grain with southern Pritania, at times with Armorica's Veneti. His captain had set out in fair weather, but after rounding the easternmost cape they ran into the great fog. They could find no haven and had to drift. They stranded on shoals near the mouth of a big river he called the Tamesis, and the rising wind and sea battered them. Then with the return of the tide, the boat was blown free, only to capsize.

All the men, a dozen like our own, clung to the hulk, but one by one slipped off to die.

"I was near to it," he said.

Simon knew this harbor of a settlement in what he said was Thanet, in easternmost Kantion. Jason asked if he wanted to be put ashore here. "Our other passengers go ashore here," he said.

"They told me you saved them from death," Simon said. "All of us owe you much."

Simon asked where we were going. When Jason told him "on north," he offered to help, at least as far as his home port. "I know this coast," he said. His eyes pleaded.

Jason and Girondas were delighted. Girondas had seen little beyond here. He had been into the great river but his knowledge was years old. "Tides and storms must have changed it many times," he said.

After supper, with the tide rising but still low, Jason, Girondas, Eban, and I took Simon ashore, Tregela, Barda, and Rob to go after cleaning up and freshening their clothes. Eban, to his dismay, was told to stay by the small boat and pull it up with the tide. "Later," Jason promised. We waded across muddy flats.

Simon franked us. He knew people and told his story. Any suspicion became friendship. These were all sailors or fishermen.

Jason was able to get fresh water, a little grain from their last winter stores, and a live sheep. He offered our Artemis coins, but their king took only one as a curiosity.

"He says who saves a sailor becomes his friend," Simon explained.

When we returned to the gaulos, the women and Rob were below deck. "Aren't they ready?" Jason asked.

Girondas called, then went below. In a few minutes he came up, looking serious. "What's the matter now?" Jason demanded.

Girondas nodded toward another part of the harbor. There was the leather boat we had seen in the Sequana, and the big man staring toward us.

"How did he get here so fast?" Jason exclaimed.

"He must know these waters. That boat is not so frail as it looks. He probably sailed like a bubble in that gale and fog. He must be a seaman. Or his captain is."

"Anybody with him?"

"He didn't follow us to haggle by himself."

Jason had his fresh supplies quickly stowed. "Let's get out of here." He snapped at me, "I told you women are nothing but trouble!"

The men, hope of fun ashore destroyed, still seemed to sense urgency. Herakles spoke to Jason, who shook his head. "He wants to swim over and cut a hole in their boat. I ought to let him."

In the slow darkness of the long evening, we raised anchor and rowed quietly to sea. Nothing was following us, we hoped.

Simon piloted us out and as soon as we were offshore, we raised sails and headed northeast. The sea breeze of night made us tack, but there was little chop and we made good progress.

I looked back. This was the solid mass our geographers thought was one of some small islands from which cassiterite and gold came. Other boats I had noted in the harbor showed there must be commerce, with the port on the Sequana, others in Pritania, and Abalus and even more northern lands. I saw two long boats Girondas said probably were Abalan.

In the market I had seen salt, and iron ornaments for harnesses. Was iron mined around here? While we were anchored, I could see both hills and flatland stretching away. Simon told us there was much more to come. This was no tiny island. This was a great land.

While Jason and Typhis kept a close watch astern, Simon made himself one of us. He quickly learned Tartessan nautical language. Girondas and I, mixing together Tartessan, Greek, Keltoi, and many signs, questioned him about lands still north. He knew that Pritania went far beyond his home, but had not sailed to the end. He had heard of that land, on beyond the tip and to the east and had seen men from there. "Light-haired, blue-eyed giants, almost as big as your Herakles." He knew Pritania to be a big island, for he had been to Belerion and had seen Okeanos from the western coast. He had heard of Ierné and its gold but had never been there. He knew nothing of the Alione captain's land on the far side of Okeanos.

While we talked, Barda came up. She looked astern and saw nothing on the horizon.

"May we come up?" she asked. Jason only nodded and resumed his watch. She called down to Tregela and Rob.

For the first time we had leisure to see them. The men all looked from their duties as much as they could. Barda herself was a strong woman, her hair graying, her face just beginning to show lines. Tregela, pale, with her hair still covered with her hood, no longer looked like a child, as small as she was. She said almost nothing. Rob, perhaps ten years old, stayed close but his eyes roved about the ship and the men.

Leonidas brought up the old leather sail and the makeshift pallets and set up their shelter in the prow again. Barda thanked him, then went aft to Jason. Girondas followed.

"We will not be idlers," she told Jason, when he turned.

"There is nothing you can do," Jason replied. "Just keep out of the way. We wanted to put you ashore back there. We were told there were paths and trails south and west and you could have walked to your realm, or taken a ship."

"You would have sent us to be killed?" she asked.

"Your quarrel is not my quarrel," Jason retorted. His anger was rising.

Girondas took her arm gently and led her forward. She was as angry as Jason, but silent with Girondas' calm restraint.

XIII

HERAKLES' SWIM

WE ROUNDED a headland and saw the land turn west, almost straight. "The big river, the Tamesis," Simon said. "If you want to go up, remember there are many shoals like what wrecked us." He said there were trading settlements on the banks and islands. Jason and I agreed to go on north. We had only about a month to solstice.

A brisk westerly breeze took us across the mouth, probably three hundred stadia wide. Simon watched for shoals and toward sunset we sighted the next headland. We passed in the dusk, blessing the long twilight. Another storm seemed making up, but Simon took us to a good anchorage an hour later in a river. We slept quietly by its low, wooded shore. There was another burst of thunderbolts, nothing like the one in Iberia.

At dawn we headed out. The tide was still flooding, and Simon had us keep the land close because the tidal current against us was less strong inshore. "After the flood we will get help," he told us. "But we still should stay close because most storms come off the land. Shoals run parallel to the shore but I know channels."

A fair wind kept us moving, although I thought impatiently that it took hours to pass a landmark. Jason reminded me of geometry. "The angle fools you."

After two days the land started to fall away west and Simon headed us northwest, across the mouth of a broad bay. A few hours later we picked up a shoreline and kept it in sight.

Simon pilots the gaulos past The Naze and into the Orwell River for overnight storm shelter. It crosses The Wash, passes the mouth of the Humber, then Dogger Bank offshore, and continues on up the coast.

"There is another large river ahead," Simon told Jason. "I know an anchorage if you want it."

But a fair wind was to be used on a sea known for sudden, violent storms. We sailed on, close in to that magnificent coast. We saw scattered settlements, and often passed small boats, some large. "The big ones go out to a shallow place where there are many fish," Simon told us. "Some small ones take lobster off the bottom inshore."

Simon hailed one fisherman. For an obol, which fascinated him, he gave us a half dozen lobsters, much bigger than the ones in Our Sea. Leonidas filled a big jar to keep them alive in sea water.

At supper Simon turned from his share of lobster to tell us his home port was two or three days ahead.

"You want to leave us there, I know," Jason said.

"I must tell wives and children."

"Do you know someone who can pilot us on north?"

"There are men."

None of us wanted to see Simon go. He now was a good friend as well as a good pilot.

Late that evening I stood at the stern rail, talking to Typhis. The night was overcast, but still light, with a following breeze. I noticed a shape astern, and after a few minutes realized it was another boat. "Call Jason," Typhis said. Jason roused quickly. "Him again!" was all he said. "Couldn't it be some other boat?" I asked. "Not a chance."

He guessed we would be overtaken in an hour. He told Typhis to hold course as if unaware, then awakened Herakles. "He can do what he wants to do." He picked up a coil of light rope. Herakles came aft grinning. He took off his robe and fastened his belt with his big knife around his body. Jason knotted a loop of the rope around his chest.

We waited. "Should I warn the women?" I asked.

"And have them screaming?"

"Oh, Jason, you haven't heard a scream yet."

"I better not."

We sailed on. Only the sound of our bow wave came to us. Then we heard the pursuing boat. Its wide, sloping bow slapped the wavelets. Its course would bring it alongside to the right.

Jason nodded and Herakles slipped into the water from our left side. He silently dove and swam under water, trailing his lifeline. We could follow him by a faint glow.

A tiny ship alone at sea.

The line stopped running through Jason's hand. "He's there."

We heard an explosion of Keltoi curses. The leather boat stopped dead. "He must have cut a huge hole," Jason said. Typhis came about to stop us. The change in our motion awoke Girondas and he came aft. "Veneti!" he said, listening to the cursing. We saw the mast fall. "He cut a stay too!" The boat swung broadside to the breeze and its stern cocked out of the water. The helmsman lost the oar and the boat was helpless. All the Veneti were shouting, at us or at each other. Our own crew awoke and sensing a fight, picked up whatever they could reach for weapons.

There was no fight. Jason felt three tugs on the rope and started hauling in. The leather boat still floated, with air trapped in folds, a shapeless mass.

When Jason had pulled Herakles back, we saw his arm around the neck of a man – the big man we had been fleeing. Herakles asked what to do with him. Jason laughed.

"Drown him, for all I care!" I understood this even in Tartessan.

"Please." Barda stood with us. "Let me handle him. He is my worthless brother and our king's. Bring him aboard."

"Are you crazy?" Jason exclaimed. "He wants to kill you."

"He will kill no one. All his valor is back there with that Veneti pirate. Himself, he is nothing." She leaned over the rail. "Do you swear, Otho, to harm no one?"

Otho gasped and Herakles tightened his hold and held him lower. Waves washed over his face. "I swear," he sputtered.

"You will do whatever your queen or your prince or I say, even jump to your death?" Herakles again squeezed.

"I swear."

"You will obey any command by anybody on this ship—even this beardless boy sailor?" Otho responded without waiting.

She turned to Jason. "He is weak in the head but he will keep his oath."

Jason had him dragged aboard and stood over him with a belaying pin. He groveled. Herakles called. Our men started to pull him up by the rope but he protested.

Leonidas turned to Barda. "Please, go to your shelter. He has no clothes on. He says hurry, the water is cold!" She laughed as she went forward, "Whatever do men think they have to hide?" Herakles came aboard and dressed.

We got under way. Astern the leather hulk drifted, its crew shouting to be saved.

"It will drift ashore in a few hours, " Simon said. "We're not far out. They can repair it and sail home."

XIV

THE ROYAL COUSINS

NOW WE COULD SLEEP. We could hear Barda telling Tregela and Rob, then all was quiet forward. Jason tied Otho's arms loosely but securely, with a leash to Herakles' wrist, and made him lie next to Herakles. The man, almost as big, still was terrified and lay as far as the leash would let him.

With morning ship routine resumed. Jason, Girondas, and Simon ignored Otho, now leashed to a stanchion, and the rest saw him only in passing. Barda, Tregela, and Rob avoided him. Leonidas gave him breakfast, but no wine. Barda had warned that wine was Otho's weakness. "Also greed. For money or a kingdom."

Barda, Tregela, and Rob watched the shoreline. Each headland gave one or another something to say to each other. I supposed it was the beauty.

That evening we came in sight of a high headland with weather threatening. Simon knew a harbor and Jason headed us in. "Our storms can give you a bad time," Simon told him. "Some of these shores wash away in great seas."

A northerly gale, the boreas, did blow up and we were glad to find the harbor, with the long headland running fifty stadia seaward to shield us.

As always entering a strange harbor, I got out of the way. I joined our passengers at the rail forward. Simon stood by their shelter to pilot us in.

Tregela began to point excitedly. "We know this kingdom!" Tregela exclaimed. These were her first voluntary words since coming aboard.

The gaulos, with its passengers, heads on and finds a gale harbor in Bridlington Bay, on the south side of Flamborough Head, in a kingdom in the Deira tribe region.

Barda smiled. "This is Deira. A cousin of our dead king is king here," she said. "We thought we must be close."

"Bless the boreas," I said. "We might have sailed by."

Tregela gestured to describe a large house, and I noticed for the first time her graceful hands. "We were there when I was little. Rob was a baby."

"We will leave you here," Barda said.

"Shall I tell Jason?"

"I will tell him."

Simon took us to a quay. When we were secure, the three went to Jason. He smiled, and I thought not entirely in relief.

"And this?" he asked, pointing to Otho, sitting dejected with his leash still fastened.

"And this." Otho brightened, then looked piteous. He saw no forgiveness.

We went ashore. Simon greeted friends and told his story. There was sadness for lost men, but disaster had touched here in other times and more closely.

Barda, Tregela, and Rob joined us soon. Their clothes were no longer ragged, and I saw that much of their time in the shelter had been spent repairing snags and rips. Leonidas must have let them use sail needles and thread and a good knife.

Tregela had freed her hair and put it in a great knot at her neck. Her father's gold chain hung on her breast. Barda stood straight. The gold-inlaid belt was around Rob's waist—almost twice. His hair no longer was a magpie's nest. Otho stood, haggard, uncertain, but erect. I guessed he wished someone would give him wine. He silently did as Barda ordered, mostly with her stern glances.

Tregela asked for the king, Wycomb, and his Queen Elsina. "We bring greetings, and sad news of our King Althos," she said.

I wondered that she, so silent aboard ship, now did the talking. Then I realized that she *was* queen, and Barda had coached her to *be* queen before these people.

They were awed, even with their curiosity about us and our strange ship. The tavern keeper sent a boy running up the hill. In time a chariot drawn by a small horse came, and the driver bowed and motioned the three to it.

Jason, seeing all friendly, had given our men shore leave, with an injunction to make and keep friends and get in no fights. Herakles led to the tavern. They had waited long.

Otho's eyes followed them until Barda shook his arm.

The driver helped Tregela into the chariot. I thought Barda would join her. She beckoned to Jason.

"You are the one to meet our cousins first," she said in Keltoi. Jason was puzzled until Girondas pushed him gently.

"Go with her."

The driver led the horse. We walked behind, Barda, Otho, Rob, Girondas, and I. I looked back and saw Eban. He had not joined the men. Girondas waved him to us.

It was a long walk for sailing men. I wished Tregela had found room for Girondas, but he kept pace easily, better than Otho. "Too much wine, too little work," I thought.

Soon ahead of us rose a stone and grass mound, a fort of upended logs on a hill. The driver led us through the gateway. Inside were a small farm, several buildings, and a large hall. We were taken to it. Bronze shields and banners hung on the wall. Animal skins lay on the dirt floor. A great table was set. I felt like Odysseus.

King Wycomb and Queen Elsina met us at the wide door. They embraced Tregela, Barda, Rob, and even Otho, although with restraint, perhaps distaste, despite the smile he managed.

Tregela presented Jason, who was ill at ease with a dialect he did not fully know. Girondas moved behind him to interpret.

"He is the one who saved us and helped us bury our king at sea," she told Wycomb and Elsina.

The story followed, with Otho hanging his head. "He fell in with evil men," Barda explained.

King Wycomb laughed over our adventure with the Veneti pirate. "You are lucky you were plucked through the hole," he told Otho. "They would have torn you to pieces for a bungler."

"He will bungle no more," Barda said. "For them, anyway."

The queen took Tregela, Barda, and Rob to bathe and put on fresh clothes. Barda said to Girondas and Jason, pointing to Otho, "No wine!" Jason smiled. "We may need Herakles." I guessed Herakles by now would be little help.

King Wycomb called in another large man and put Otho in his custody. "Clean him up and get him clothes," he told the guard. "Let him drink nothing but water. "Watch him – he may be dangerous yet!" The guard led a humble Otho away.

King Wycomb told us about his cousin Althos. He seemed familiar with affairs in southern Pritania. "We all have blood ties," he said, waving to tell of kings to the south. "Words go up and down the coast."

He told us that King Althos' realm was in the Durotrige region on that southern coast, between Belerion and Kantion. Althos tried to find ways to get around the Veneti monopoly on cassiterite trade for his merchants and artisans.

Tregela was born, his first child, followed a year later by a son who died in infancy. Persuaded by Otho, who had often gone to Armorica and other parts of Keltika, Althos did what many high-born did with young children, made a marriage pact for Tregela, with a small Veneti nobleman, in hope that this would help with trade.

"It didn't, of course," Wycomb said. "The Veneti ignored the bond and ignored Althos. Otho was just his tool. Meanwhile this child grew to be the lovely young woman you see today. Althos was sorry. He loved her too well now to let her go to another land. Rob had been born, but their mother died in childbirth. Barda became their mother, forgoing any hope she might have had of marrying."

In time, Althos came to suspect that Otho's counsel was tainted with ambitions not his own.

"This nobleman was really a pirate – probably the one you sank," Wycomb said, "and also generous with wine, and like a fool Otho joined him."

"Otho was insistent and Althos finally agreed to go ahead, the marriage ceremony to be in his own hill-fort. Tregela trusted her father but in her young way felt that her uncle was arranging what would only make her unhappy. She pleaded to visit the Veneti's home first. That was the reason for their voyage. It was Althos' own little boat – he loved to sail and probably thought nothing of crossing to Armorica. Otho likely followed in another boat to make sure. He may have thought the Veneti was going to pay him for a bride."

"We are sure we saw Otho in the Sequana," Girondas told him.

"He no doubt lost them in the fog and went on," the king said. "Probably saw the Veneti in the Sequana and told him they were trying to run away. Then when you came in, he suspected you had them aboard and got the Veneti to follow. He is not smart but he is wilful and wicked."

"Never underrate fools," Girondas sighed.

"If Althos had talked to you years ago, he would be alive in his realm today." He turned to Jason and added, "You see, captain, you have helped right a great wrong."

"I thought Tregela and Rob and Barda were wreckers," Jason admitted. "I learned better just in time."

"And now they must return at once–under guard. Tregela must hasten to claim her realm and tell her people about Althos."

We heard running steps and the guard rushed in. "He got away!" he exclaimed. "I turned my head for a second!" Wycomb laughed, to the relief of the guard.

"Take a horse to the tavern," he said. "And a sword!"

The guard went out and we heard hoof-beats.

Wycomb took us to wash up for the feast we saw on the table. We came back, and soon Queen Elsina led Tregela, Barda, and Rob into the hall. Tregela's face, now free of shipboard grime, glowed; her eyes, though still red from salt, shone. Her too large borrowed robes had been gathered and fastened. Barda looked even more regal. Elsina's clothes fitted her well. Rob glowered. He had had to put on a woman's jacket, there being no boy here. The smell of food lightened his brow.

Wycomb told of Otho's escape. "We'll have him back." We soon did, again a breathless, humiliated man, a sword at his back.

"He was running back up the hill, with a black-bearded giant chasing him," the guard said. "He never got in the tavern door."

"Good man," Jason smiled. "My boatswain."

Barda made Otho sit beside her. First she emptied his beaker back into the big jar that held the day's supply. "Curmi would make you an even bigger fool than wine," she frowned.

"Curmi is their grain drink," Girondas told me. "A lot like that brew the Abalan traders gave us on the Sequana."

"I am warned," I said.

We feasted long into the evening. Wycomb's kitchen had prepared a great meal on short notice. It included cold cuts from a large animal tasting better than lamb or goat. "We did not have time to hunt and roast

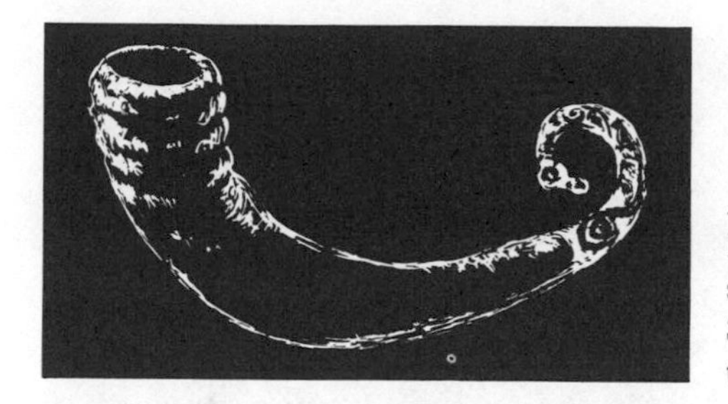

A drinking horn such as Pytheas might have used. The silver tip was found in Scotland, and dates to the third century B.C.

one anew for you," Wycomb said. He showed the head, with branched horns.

Food, even with no drink, revived Otho. He talked easily with any who would listen. Even Barda smiled, though warily.

"He is a charmer," she told Jason and me. "He can charm the beard off your face. Why does he have to be a fool too? And a dangerous one."

At the end we were shown to chambers to sleep on soft mats that did not rise, fall, or roll. I was surprised how I missed that. As I drowsed off, I realized too that I could follow and even speak the Keltoi dialects better. I still had to turn to Girondas, but less often. Jason had picked up this one soon. Tregela helped him with gentle–and welcome–corrections.

Darkness was short and my conscience awoke me at dawn. Others were awake, too. Horses stomped and harness jangled. A servant brought hot gruel, but I could hear the gale still blowing through the trees and knew I must use our stay in port. I aroused Eban and we ate quickly.

I awoke Girondas and asked him to tell the king we had science to do, and Eban and I rushed to the ship. I wanted to start the water-clock with sunrise and had to leave Eban tending it. He was disappointed not to go wherever I was going, but Leonidas and the crew were in no shape for science. Simon was awake and sober, but he had never seen a water-clock. I asked him to help me with shore observations of people, animals, birds, plants–whatever we might see.

I took my gnomon and told Eban he could go the next time. We passed Wycomb's hill-fort again, and found Jason leaning against a stone wall, Tregela not far away watching grooms and horses. She explained that

Pritania's grain.

Wycomb was getting an armed caravan ready, to leave next dawn. He came out. "We'll see that they get there."

"We don't have armies," he added, "but we do have men to fight off robbers – or stranded pirates. Good men, handy with swords, bows, spears, or staves – or fists. They can stop with other kings in their forts at night."

I asked if Tregela's kingdom would be safe, with King Althos gone and nobody there knowing of his fate.

"My grandfather reigns when the king is gone," she said. "He will allow no one to come except in peace."

"He also knows Otho well," Wycomb laughed. "He tried to warn Althos but couldn't harden his heart."

We took a path to the eastern end of the headland. I looked back and saw Jason talking to Tregela. Both sat on the wall.

As we walked, Simon pointed out round shepherds' huts, sheep with wool coarser than I had seen, many new lambs, and small fields where grain was feathering through the ground. Blossoms were underfoot and every glade was a bower. I thought of Persephone returning to the upper world and Demeter keeping her grateful promise to show mankind when to till the soil.

How plants responded to the long days and twilights between the Pleiades and the Dog Star! Yet winter nights, when Persephone is with Pluto, must be as long.

This was my first land exploration and I was delighted at so many new things. There was a feeling of vastness. Some land we crossed was gaunt, some fertile dale. There were sea birds everywhere, many following farmers tilling fields, myriads more diving for fish in the waves on the southern side of the headland. Simon said the sea was shallow and full of fish.

At the point, we set up my gnomon to await noon. The gale was even stronger here and the sea below was a heaving froth. The horizon was lost in mist, but the sun sparkled off wave crests. Trees bent and grass lay almost flat.

We could see another ship being driven in by the gale. It was a long one, with many oars. Men were busy bringing goods from below deck. Simon said it probably was from the land to the east, with traders to take their wares, possibly including elektron, overland to Belerion or a port to ship on to Iernê. I hoped they would be in our harbor when we got back. Simon thought they might join Tregela's caravan.

At noon Simon held the gnomon against the wind and I found we were

Bronze shield.

a little more than fifty-four degrees – twelve north of Massalia. I watched the tide. The cliff rose clear from the waves when we arrived, but in time a rocky beach began to show. There were places where pieces of cliff had fallen. Simon said that at low tide the beach was very wide.

On our way back we stopped at an inn, where a few farmers and shepherds were resting. They offered us a drink Simon said was made from fermented honey. I took a little cautiously. They smiled at my effort to speak their dialect, but Simon said they were glad I tried.

"These people are much like my own in Bernicia," he said. "We are only a little farther north of here."

The small farms all had several buildings, and Simon said both animals and grain had to be sheltered against winter rains and snows. I knew of much snow in mountains of Greece and Italy and on Iberian peaks west of Massalia, and we often had it at Massalia. Here it was heavy every winter, Simon said. Even threshing in harvest time had to be done indoors because of rain, with doors set over cubit-high sills to keep grain in and let flailed chaff blow out.

Spring looked as far along here as at Kantion, though the sea water was cold. Hyperborean regions might not be so terrible. I wondered about climate over the years. At the inn shepherds had mentioned, and Simon confirmed, old legends of far colder winters.

When we returned to the hill-fort, the caravan was almost ready. Jason was just coming up the hill from the ship, where he had made sure all was still secure. The gale had not yet blown itself out. King Wycomb made a last inspection of the chariots or carts, loaded with weapons and shields, robes, skins, food, and utensils. The two women and Rob would ride horses, Otho also but under guard.

Eban and I worked on our observations. He timed the sun's hours carefully by the water-clock, and as much as he wanted to join me and Girondas on exploration of the settlement after supper, he refused to leave his watch to Simon or Leonidas, now recovered from his shore revels.

Girondas, Simon, and I walked about, surprised to see more chariot-like carts, almost like those the Persians use in war. The people here did not seem war-like, and the carts appeared more useful for horses or oxen to haul grain or firewood. Still, Girondas picked up a story, with Simon's help, that these people descended from a tribe of Keltoi who had come from the eastern side of the sea and who buried their royal dead in chariots. This might explain the traders joining the caravan; their custom might reach back for generations.

Along the harbor beaches were hide boats like those of the Veneti of that same eastern mainland much farther south. Also along the beaches we picked up beautiful stones, some shiny black, others carnelian. Girondas learned the black stones were mined nearby and valued as ornaments, much like elektron at home.

The gale died out but we slept lightly on the ship. Jason was first awake and impatient to get up the hill to the fort. He ate a little gruel and honey but said cheese and wine could wait. He walked on ahead of Simon, Girondas, Eban, and me.

We found the caravan assembling. A half dozen armed riders were ready ahead of Tregela, Barda, and Rob, and a half dozen more to follow closely, surrounding Otho. A cook and serving men and equipment were next. The traders lined up after them, their goods in carts apparently kept here.

Jason was talking to Tregela, and Barda had turned away. Tregela greeted us. "Ours is a sad journey," she said, "but without you and your ship there would have been only death."

"Again, we thank whatever gods put us close," Girondas said.

We heard Tregela say to Jason, "I will see you again, in our realm." Jason smiled and touched her outstretched hand.

King Wycomb and Queen Elsina embraced their cousins, except Otho. The leader raised his arm, then dropped it. The caravan started to move. Jason stood with us silently. We all watched the line turn around a bend in the wooded trail and leave only the last traders in sight.

"The ebb starts at noon," Jason said. "We sail then."

XV

SIMON'S DUTY

WE GOT AWAY with the tide and as soon as we rounded the cliff we were in bumpy swells left by the gale. The wind was fitful from the west, so we could sail only part of the time. When it died, the men rowed to keep us steady if not moving fast.

By morning the weather settled again with a fair southwesterly wind as we headed northwesterly along the coast. Simon said little beyond calling landmarks. He stood at the prow, thinking, we knew, of what to say to eleven women and their children. Our men knew that he still understood little Tartessan, but they held off on their usual ribald banter.

We passed a large settlement, and Simon told us sailors there hunted whales and made whale oil for trading with southern settlements. "Some of our men hunt whales, too," he said. Girondas mentioned the Iberian whale hunters, and Simon said, "We meet them once in a while. They are great sailors." Then he added with a smile, "Like you Tartessans."

The coast bent more westerly and Simon saw marks that meant home. The greatest was the cliff—as Simon had told us, the highest we would see. It looked close to a stadium high. He led us in to an anchorage by a settlement much like others. The tide was rising but too low to get to a quay.

"Take him ashore, Eban," Jason said. Simon embraced Jason and Herakles, held his arms to all, and stepped into the skiff.

Ashore Simon walked slowly. In Tartessan robes he was not recognized at once. Then friends crowded around. Soon he moved on alone.

Simon pilots the gaulos past Whitby, where Captain James Cook learned to be a sailor in our eighteenth century, then on to his own home in Staithes, in the tribal region of Bernicia.

The people at the waterfront gathered in little groups. Here as everywhere, disaster was a reminder of disaster.

After an hour, two men poled out. Girondas greeted them. He turned to us. "They ask us all ashore."

Girondas went with them, and Eban rowed Jason and me, then returned for others.

The people, men with a few somber older women, gathered around us. Girondas described Simon's rescue. He pointed to Eban, Herakles, Jason, and Typhis, then the rest of us.

The king, a tall, gaunt man close to Girondas' age, embraced us one by one, Herakles most strongly, and spoke slowly. What he said was plain from his face, his voice, and his gestures.

"He welcomes us," Girondas said. "He tells us to know this as our home as long as we stay. Whatever we want will be ours if they have it."

"Tell him we need little," Jason said. "And our sorrow is that there were no others to save." These were his first words, except for sailing orders, since leaving Wycomb's realm. I felt that much of his thought was winding south with the caravan.

We moved the gaulos to the quay with high tide and made ready to sail at next dawn. Simon and his wife and two children, a boy about Eban's age and a girl a year or so younger, came to us in late afternoon. He returned his borrowed robes.

"I had to see you again," he said. "My family wanted to see you too." His wife spoke a few words, then wept. "She thanks you," Simon said, "but bears the grief of all."

"We are sailors. We know grief," Jason said.

"Did you find a man to help you on?" Simon asked.

"We did not try. Your people have lost enough."

"You are seamen. The risk is small. Please do not leave until I come back."

Simon returned with a younger man. "He will go with you," Simon told Jason. "He has sailed this sea as far as our land goes. He knows the islands and there are many there."

"Does he know what we are doing?" Jason asked. "There will be no profit for any of us."

"I told him."

"Does he have a family?"

"No."

"Can he get home if we go beyond this land?"

"There are always ships sailing this coast."

Jason accepted the man warmly. Girondas interpreted and instructed. We called him Ogg, our rendering of his name as Simon gave it. He brought his belongings in a woolen robe.

At dawn, as we cast off, Simon came again.

"Do not forget me," he said. "I will not forget you."

I gave him an elektron locket for his wife, a knife for his boy, a bracelet for his daughter, a bronze cup for himself. "You have been a good shipmate," I told him.

He stood on the quay, watching as Ogg piloted us out. The rising sun showed him still there as we rounded for the open sea.

XVI

THE HAEMODAE AND SOLSTICE

OGG, LIKE SIMON, knew coastal marks, shoals, and havens. He also knew ship handling. The men accepted him. He was given the steering oar occasionally, and after getting the feel of the gaulos, he steered as well as Typhis or Jason. This gave Jason more time to watch ahead.

After two days sailing generally northwest, Ogg told us we were near a wide inlet, with harbors. We were still well supplied and kept on. We had had mostly fair winds, so far no more gales. There had been heavy rain, some little but thick mist.

On clear nights Jason, Eban, and I lay on deck watching stars. Again, as far north as we were, we did not seem to be getting the cold we expected. The heavy dew and mists chilled us in the breeze, but we did not suffer.

We saw Arktos stand higher and higher, swinging around the three stars above our North Pole. One dark, calm night Eban and I sighted these stars with my cross-staff for a fair reading of our latitude. Our familiar stars dropped below the southern horizon. Nights got shorter, with the approach of solstice and with our progress north.

Often we saw what I had seen only rarely at Massalia, Jason never at Gadeira. This was a pulsing, many-colored light radiating from the north. "I used to see it on northern voyages," Girondas said. "Sometimes it spreads like fingers over most of the sky." Ogg said sailors here saw it

---

Ogg pilots the gaulos across the Firth of Forth, passing the Isle of May, Fife Ness, and St. Andrews Bay, then into the Firth of Tay for provisons. He mentions marks ahead such as Moray Firth, Duncansby Head, then the Orkney Islands, and the stone circles of Maes Howe, Ring of Brodgar, and Stones of Stennis in the Orkneys, and others on Fetlar and Unst of the Shetlands. The ship clears Buchan Ness and finds gale shelter at Wick. Then it sails by the Orkneys, passes Fair Isle, and raises Sumburgh Head, southernmost point on the Shetlands. Finally it makes harbor at Unst, the northernmost port.

often. "He says landsmen fear it as spirits or gods," Girondas added.

Some nights I scarcely slept in my eagerness to know all I could about these skies. Day sleeping was uncertain, too. The shores to our left kept me awake by their beauty and by my work to put them on my map. Jason scanned them, but with concern. He and Girondas were far from their known waters. Ogg's reassurances made them no less wary.

At the last headland before the wide inlet, Ogg headed us north. We passed a small island, then picked up another headland. Still another wide bay opened to our left and Ogg suggested going in a deep inlet beyond for more food, before heading up a long coast with few harbors. He took us to a settlement where Jason bought more grain, cheese, dried fish, and two lambs. The people looked doubtfully at our money. We were beyond Philip's and Alexander's fame, though neither would have believed it possible. The people gladly took our trading goods.

Ogg told them who we were. "He makes quite a story of it," Girondas laughed. "We are all heroes and bring greetings of great kings." Ogg told of Simon's rescue. While these people were different from those of Ogg's country, they too lived with the sea, listened closely, and gazed at Herakles.

We made fine time up the coast bending northeast. The steady southerly winds pushed us as fast as we could go. (Jason tried vainly to explain why a boat could go only so fast no matter how strong the wind. I have much to learn about physics!) We now had two weeks until solstice and were grateful for our progress.

"Ogg says we are lucky," Girondas reported. "They do not always have so much good weather. He says we will round another headland, go northwest again across a wide bay, then come to the end of this coast. Then islands, the Orcades and Haemodae. And I mentioned those stone circles down in Albion. He says there are several on the Orcades and Haemodae."

I asked if they might have something to do with the heavens.

"He says there are stories handed down that ancient wise men or priests sighted the sun and moon at special times over these stones."

"What special times?"

"I suppose solstice, equinox, the farthest north or south the moon moves, even eclipses."

I wanted to visit all these circles but decided to settle for just one, now anyway, that Ogg said was on Orcas, the northernmost Haemodae. We might be there for solstice. For once Jason did not have to remind me, as so often before, that after summer came equinox and its gales, then winter, and we were a long way from Massalia!

At Ogg's suggestion Jason had bought a reed cage of land birds at our last stop. "He says we ought to keep offshore after crossing this bay because the shores are so rugged and the tides so high. When we let a bird go, it will head for land."

It took us two days to cross the bay, once we rounded the easternmost headland and headed northwest again. Jason released a bird a day and each flew westward.

Late the second day the weather turned to rain in a rising, cold northeasterly wind. Jason asked for a harbor. Ogg headed us west, easing the strain on boat and sail. A bird flew straight ahead. We could see little, but Ogg seemed sure.

Before dark we did sight the rocky coast and Ogg led us into a protected cove. Jason's faith in Ogg rose.

"How in the world did he know?" I asked Jason.

"Same as I would know near Gadeira or Onuba. A sailor knows his own seas."

As elsewhere, the cove had a small settlement of fishermen and shepherds. Girondas soon learned that the bad weather might last three days or more. As Pasias had counseled—patience! Jason kept busy and kept the men busy. The sail again was inspected closely, the rigging tightened, chafed ropes replaced, and at low tide, the bottom cleaned.

Girondas, Eban, and I explored ashore in rain and wind. Jason again let Eban off the boat work, a future captain to profit now by learning.

We found a quiet people. They lived in round, fort-like stone buildings, some with two or three floors, reached by ladders, some mostly underground. Cattle and sheep could be sheltered on the ground floor or in walled pens that held out the wind in winter, and where grain was threshed at harvest time. Each building was large enough for several families. "They call them brochs," Girondas said after talking to a man.

There was a lovely green over the hills, and a few trees. Fields were planted with millet for their bread, and also for their fermented drink. (Does no one grow wine grapes?) Shepherds tended flocks.

At a stream crossing we came to another settlement and saw a young woman drawing water from a well. Suddenly I realized how much we all missed our women! This one was cordial and beautiful even though pale, blue-eyed, and with wisps of yellow hair slipping out of her hood. (Along Our Sea, almost all women have dark hair, dark eyes.) She offered us a drink. We accepted, though the steady rain did not let us get thirsty. Girondas tried to talk to her in Keltoi. We thought she understood, but she only murmured shyly.

"You should have talked to her, Eban," Girondas said. "She is young."

"For her I could learn Keltoi," Eban said softly, "or any tongue!" He gazed as she carried her pitcher home. I gazed too.

"Oh, to drop sixty years!" Girondas slapped us both on our backs.

We had walked far from the harbor. Girondas made friends and we were invited to stay the night in a broch. It was a filling if plain supper, with porridge, mutton roasted over a smoky fire, and bread, and the fermented drink. I was coming to like it, though still cautiously. The men ate together, served by the women. The women contrived errands to see three men from a world they had never heard of.

This broch was a tall, round-walled affair, with an underground structure close by. We slept under a shelter outside the wall with the herdsmen. The women, again making errands, showed us to straw beds, then returned giggling to the building through the single door, which the men barred. Despite rainclouds, the night never got dark. But we were tired, the straw was soft and dry, and we slept. So did the shepherds, all snoring loudly.

We returned to the harbor in the morning, the rain stopping but the wind still strong. We found Jason and the gaulos ready to sail whenever the weather broke. He had picked up more food and water and even let Herakles fill an amphora with the grain drink. "He will not try to drink it all," Jason said.

I used our waiting time sketching my map. Simon had told me of the shores he knew, and Girondas drew more from Ogg. Pritania and this new land seemed to be one or possibly two big islands. Ogg was not sure how far into the land these inlets reached. He thought this second might run through to the western side and that narrow sea. "He says men come from the southwest," Girondas reported, "but he is not sure they come by boat all the way."

The whole mass, judging from what we could learn of the western side, was triangular, with the apex to the north, the east-west base to the south. We had no idea how Iernê might lie.

We finally got away and Ogg headed us north. A golden sunlight

Underground shelter of a Scottish broch.

warmed us if not the sea, and the wind was fair again. "He says there are enough islands to follow for several days," Girondas told us. So we kept on, past the rocky Orcades. We kept them in sight but gave a wide berth on Ogg's warnings of tides and currents. We came to open sea again, headed more northeasterly, passed a small island, and after a day raised another headland. Ogg said it was the southernmost of the Haemodae and that two days' sail should take us to the northernmost. "He says that is as far as he has ever been."

Two days, and we had five to solstice. May the wind hold fair!

It did, for a day. Then we had a misty calm. The sea was as flat as our Massalia harbor. The men rowed, but we seemed to move so slowly. I could feel time running away.

"Patience, patience," Girondas said. "You are farther than any Greek has ever been. A few stadia make little difference."

"But the prize is in sight," I sighed.

"We'll get to it," Jason said, "if this calm doesn't bring on something bad." Ogg did not think bad weather likely but admitted it could change quickly.

I tried to calm myself by watching seabirds and dolphins. Thousands and thousands of birds flew from the islands. We could see no trees ashore, but the birds probably nested on the ground or in holes in the brilliantly colored cliffs. Some cliffs looked more than a stadium high.

The dolphins played around the gaulos. They came to the tips of the oars but never touched. We were their toy.

Girondas called to me and pointed right. I saw nothing, then a fountain five or six stadia away. "A whale," he said. "There are hundreds here, Ogg says. Look–there are more!"

"Hundreds!" I exclaimed. I had seen one only occasionally in Our Sea. Now fountains spurted all about us.

I watched while one huge fish raised its wide, divided tail and dived. "He will come up somewhere," Girondas added. "He breathes air. He is not a fish. He just went down to fill his belly." One leaped clear of the sea.

"I hope he doesn't come up under us," Jason said. One did rise within a half stadium. He was more than our length.

I could have watched them for hours, but an easterly breeze started us sailing again. Ogg called off island after hilly island. The main island was long, but smaller ones came in sight. Jason was wary of sailing at night, especially with an onshore breeze, but the twilight was so long and the actual night so short that we never lost the islands. Ogg watched carefully and the breeze was light enough to keep us at a safe speed. But we could see heavy surf against the shores and their boulders. We also could see scores of seals, much like those of Our Sea, watching us from beaches and rocks.

At last Ogg headed us in. Again, he knew where and took us around an arm of land to a cove with a settlement. "This is the farthest good harbor," he told Girondas. "We are safe unless a gale comes out of the north. This is Orcas."

We moored late in the day. The calm had stretched our last sail to the day before solstice. Now we had only hours. Jason was most interested but did ask, echoing Girondas, "One day or another, only a minute longer or shorter, will you know the difference?"

"But I have to see," I protested.

We went ashore on the bleak and treeless island. People of a settlement much like the last greeted us. They were curious but friendly, once Ogg assured them we were not from the east. Our gaulos was a strange craft and we were from a land they did not know existed. They lived by fish and mutton and wool, and kept their heads dry in stone brochs like those to the south.

Ogg confirmed that there were three stone circles on Orcas and walked

A whale rose close to the gaulos.

with Eban, Girondas, a native, and me to see them. Almost nowhere were we out of sight of the sea, the one we had been sailing to the east, Okeanos west . . . what to the north? We found the circles in the long twilight and I set up my gnomon in one. "If these have anything to do with the stars," I told Girondas, "maybe I will see it." Ogg and the native talked at length, and Girondas picked up enough to tell me, "These people do use these circles. There is to be a ceremony here tomorrow. You may have to move the gnomon."

I asked if I should now.

The native seemed little concerned, but Ogg told Girondas that Orcas' king might be. I moved it outside the circle.

As we returned, a feeling of vastness, of the sea and sky, came over me anew. It was beautiful here, in a stark way, but I missed trees. Yet it was no time for philosophizing. At the gaulos I brought out the sand-glass for tomorrow, and set up the water-clock on the quay. Typhis would start it at sunrise.

When dusk finally began, Eban and I took my cross-staff to the top of a hill and waited for our polar stars. We had had a supper of porridge, milk, mutton, and a small fish these people caught in great numbers. I wanted olives but Leonidas said the supply was low. We still had Meton's good wine.

The polar stars were long in appearing because of the twilight and we had a misty sea horizon. With only rough sights, we found we must be more than sixty degrees north of the equator. I pressed Jason again for a guess at how many stadia north we had sailed, but he begged off. "Those currents, the calms, the storms . . . I could be a thousand stadia wrong and never know it." Nor was I able to guess how far west we might be from a north-south line through Massalia. As Girondas had suggested, my Dryas might be the one to make that calculation someday. I felt sure that that line was much closer here to one through Oestrymnis than the same lines in that latitude.

Neither Eban nor I slept under a moon one or two days past the first quarter. We were thinking too much. Often he asked a question in a low voice. I had learned long ago that he rarely asked twice, once we had mastered enough of each other's language. I came to think that this beardless boy might in time tell us Greeks how to measure our world if Jason could keep him out of the mines.

As the night's thin darkness faded, I aroused Typhis and Girondas. For all the weariness that must be in him, Girondas was going with us. Jason awoke too. Our excitement was infecting him, partly because of his own curiosity. He may have seemed indifferent yesterday, but not now.

Leonidas had left cold porridge and milk, and lunches of cheese, dried fish, and the coarse bread he had learned to bake. Ogg said he would come later, and went back to sleep. Nobody else stirred.

As we walked to the ring, men joined us. Among them was one Ogg had pointed out as king, living in the largest broch. He and Girondas talked easily.

"He says this circle where you first set up the gnomon tells them the day of summer solstice," Girondas told me.

"I'm glad we moved it."

"He wouldn't have minded. He wants to see you use it. For a week they have come out at sunrise. When the sun lines up with a special stone and that peak there, they know it is the day."

"What about the other circles?" I asked.

"One tells winter solstice."

"And the third?"

Flowers of a northern clime.

"He does not know. They were erected long before anybody remembers and probably were used by men who left before the ancestors of these people came."

I began to feel that these stones might have told ancient priests much, even how to predict eclipses or celestial movements. If their people worshipped the sun or moon or both, the priests would gain power, especially if they kept their knowledge secret. Yet, how could they?

More evidence that neither Greeks, Egyptians, Babylonians, Chaldeans, nor whoever came before them invented learning. How far back does it go? How often has it been lost? What is still lost?

We arrived a few minutes before sunrise. We joined the king at the special stone. Eban held the sand-glass, ready to turn.

The sun rose, perfectly in line with the peak. The king bowed and spoke a prayer. His people did likewise. Jason and Girondas bowed to the sun as their Tartessan god. I remembered Apollo. I also thought of Anticlea and wished she could be with me for this day. She might be awake now, for the sun must have risen already over Massalia. But how much earlier? How many degrees to the east? How many stadia in a degree of longitude this far north?

Our next work was measuring the angle of the sun's shadow at noon. Eban turned the sand-glass and marked a sheet of papyrus. The king stayed a while and was as curious about the sand-glass as the gnomon. "He says they tell time during the day only by the sun," Girondas told us. "At night Arktos tells all they need to know. Hours do not matter. But he will come back before noon."

We watched life about the island, much of which was in sight. There were shepherds. A woman was busy in a flock near a broch, combing rather than shearing for the fine wool. On beaches women gathered driftwood to burn.

Other animals grazed. Small horses with shaggy coats looked almost as if they too might yield wool. There were small cattle. "He says their meat is very good," Girondas told us after talking to a man. "The cows are milked the same as sheep. Maybe we can buy a bull for the gaulos, already slaughtered, though."

Small barley fields had been planted, although the soil did not look rich for bountiful crops. Near the brochs were small gardens growing mostly root vegetables.

"I suppose the grain goes for the drink as much as for bread," I said to Girondas.

"Do you bake bread with grapes?"

As the sun neared zenith, we kept close to the gnomon. The king came back. Eban and I watched intently. We placed a pebble at the shadow end every few seconds and a shallow curve grew.

The curve stopped. Eban stopped the glass. We estimated how much sand had run. Eban marked the figure, then started the glass again quickly. The pebble line now began to curve away to the east. We measured to the closest pebble. We calculated our angle. We were almost sixty-two degrees north.

And the world went on.

XVII

WHICH WAY?

ALL THE LONG AFTERNOON we explored about the circles, with Eban carefully carrying the sand-glass level and turning it. The upright stones threw long, soft shadows, so unlike the sharp shadows of the brilliant sun of Our Sea. The circle for the winter solstice was interesting and Girondas said, "I suppose you want to stay for that too."

"Massalia's winter nights are long enough."

"These people live through winter," he reminded me.

"And Aristotle doesn't think anybody can up here."

"He can't know everything from Athens."

"I can't even know everything right here."

But what next, what next? Girondas and I had questioned the king about what lay on to the north. Ogg was at the farthest reach of his knowledge, but had heard of other lands. The king confirmed that his island was not the end of Earth.

"He says three or four days' sail to the east is a land," Girondas reported. "It is big and rugged and the people are warlike. Sometimes they sail here to rob and pillage, but mostly farther south where there are more people and more wealth. Then he says three or four days' sail northwest there are more islands much like these and on beyond them he thinks there is a large land where nobody lives but mountain fires burn."

"Didn't that Alione captain tell about that?" I asked.

The king of Orcas (Unst, Shetland Islands) mentions Norway to the east, the Faeroes northwest, and Iceland beyond, as well as desolate Jan Mayen island far to the north. The gaulos goes on northwest after the solstice observations, approaches the Faeroes' eastern island of Svinoy, and the men see thousands of sea birds, with skuas pirating fish from them. Weather prevents stopping, and the gaulos goes on toward Iceland, to be blocked by floating ice, ground small by wave action.

"Probably the same place. But the king says nobody goes that far. What the lands to the east or beyond the islands northwest are called, he does not know."

"What is straight on north?"

"Nothing," he says. "Except, he has heard of a rugged, desolate island far, far up there. He thinks that if it exists, it must be surrounded by frozen water most of the year. No one would want to live there or even go there, he says."

"Only some geographer like me."

"Somebody must have, or he would never have heard of it."

That desolate island . . . how far? A week's sail, two weeks', how many? The Aesymnète had ordered me to "sail to the ends of the earth." But a round earth had no ends. Wherever you go, you hear of land, and people, farther on. We think *we* discover!

While we waited for sunset, I kept thinking about it. Girondas slept on the turf, probably wearier than I knew. Eban concentrated on the sandglass. He wanted to be sure the sun took exactly as long to drop to the western horizon as to climb to the zenith. It did and daylight was found to be nineteen hours.

Leonidas brought us a hearty supper of meat from one of the small cattle, more bread and cheese, and wine. Meton's wine must travel well. Not all does.

Jason came out again later. I asked what he had learned around the quay.

"They tell me Ogg did well to keep us out of the passages between these islands," he reported. "The currents are fast, the rocks many, and the tides very high and very low. The gaulos right now is on the bottom, far from water. At full or new moon and with a storm, high tides can sweep over low islands."

I had estimated the islands with people on them to be sixty to seventy cubits high, but no wonder the low ones were uninhabited.

"Did anyone say why it is warm here?" I asked. "All we had heard in Massalia was that Hyperborean regions were very cold, summer or winter."

"Nobody was sure. They think that to the east it is much colder in winter. It gets cold enough here, though, they say."

Girondas recalled his grandfather telling what he had heard from his own grandfather, that Pritania and Ierné had long been blessed with a climate warmer than on the eastern continent.

"They found that some current warmer than the rest of Okeanos came from the southwest and west," he said. "You remember that Alione captain mentioned one helping him home to Iberia. That may be the answer."

Jason, Girondas, and I debated best use for the three months to equinox the next morning. Eban listened, with Ogg occasionally offering comment or a fact.

The more we talked, the more I wanted to go farther. The weather seemed good and we might not get another such period.

"Where to?" Jason asked.

"Until we have to turn around. I was going to call this land Thule, the end, but Earth goes on. Thule is farther."

Jason hesitated. I knew he felt he must go where I wanted to go, but that he also knew how much we could do.

"The men will go where I tell them," he said. "But I cannot stretch their faith."

We agreed to sail north, or whatever direction we had to go, for two weeks. Then if we had found nothing to call Thule, we would try to return to Pritania. "That should still give us time to get south, maybe even back to Our Sea, before winter." Jason added again, "If we are lucky."

"So far," I said, "you and the men have made all our good luck. And tempered our bad."

Ogg was willing. He was an adventurer.

After talking with the king, we decided to head northwest, first for the islands he said were three or four days' sail. "The seas can be rough and those islands are rocky and hard to find in fog and rain," he warned, "but we do go there and those people sail here." His information on the distant northern island was too vague.

We rowed to sea on the next high tide. There was little breeze and we moved slowly past the northern tip of the island and headed northwest. A southwesterly breeze then started us sailing well. The sun warmed us and again it seemed like a good way to live. We sailed easily for the rest of the day and night.

Jason watched our wake always. "We must be crossing that warm current," Girondas told him. "We are probably being pushed a little northeast." Jason headed more westerly.

The sun left us and we went through showers and squalls that often forced us to lower sail. "The king did say it rained a lot around those islands," Girondas recalled as we watched a rainbow form.

At the end of the second day Jason released a caged bird. It flew south of west. "We are too far north," he said.

But the wind came around to the southeast and we could make for a tall cloud column that Girondas said must mark land. And thousands of sea birds again told us we were nearing the islands. They dived and shrieked, with large brown predatory birds about a cubit long darting to steal fish from smaller ones. Often they succeeded, occasionally were driven off. I counted a score or more species never seen on Our Sea.

We had to endure calms almost as much as squalls. Jason was uneasy when we had to row. "I like to sail." So did we all.

In two more days we sighted what we guessed to be the easternmost island. We could not be sure. We had had nothing but overcast skies, no way of telling north. High cliffs in the distance often disappeared in rain. Jason, Ogg, and Girondas stood at the prow, looking for a harbor. I tried to sketch the land but had to leave blank space.

As we got closer, we saw that although the sea was moderate where we were, surf beat hard and high against the cliffs. Waves broke on hidden rocks between us and the cliffs. Many seals lay on larger rocks.

"The king said there were harbors on this side," Girondas said, "but I sure don't see any." Nor did Ogg. "Ogg thinks in this weather it is a good place to stay away from."

"Just what I think," Jason said.

In time we cleared the islands on the north and let what we hoped was still a fair wind take us northwest. I had to content myself with the thought that it would have been nice to add knowledge, but nicer away from those shores. People there knew the sea about them, but we didn't.

The clouds broke up enough later to let a little sunshine tell us we were heading as we wanted. Again I admired Jason and Typhis for achieving a good course after being whipped by squalls and drifting in calms with the prow pointing nowhere unless the men rowed.

Our southeast breeze was steady. We had enough sun and starlight between clouds to keep us oriented. Frequent showers let Leonidas fill our amphorae, including those we had emptied of Meton's wine. "It isn't wine," he said, "but it will do." Herakles was hoarding his fermented drink, letting the other men have only sips, taking no more himself. "He

In strange waters.

wants to make it last back to the Urium," Leonidas laughed. "Probably going to try to make it at home."

"He'll have to steal grain from the Carthaginians," Jason said.

"He'll enjoy that, too."

"He'd better remember that his size is all that keeps him out of the mines. They can still make him a pack mule."

We found the air cooler. The short nights even seemed cold. "Maybe we are really getting to your Hyperborean country," Jason said to me. One day when the breeze swung northwest to head us, we felt a definite sharpness. "It's from some place cold," Jason said. "Maybe your Thule."

It came back to southeast and we kept on our course and again saw towering clouds ahead. "That land of fire must be close," Girondas said. More thousands of sea birds told us that too.

But the air thickened with another low cloud of fog. The wind dropped. Soon we were in a dead calm. Jason set the men to rowing slowly. He watched our wake closely, for we could see nothing ahead.

Then, first in small patches, later in wider, we began to move into the strange floating, soft, white stuff that looked like a shoal of our sea lungs. Here and there were hard chunks. The men rowed even more slowly. Now and then one missed a stroke when his oar hit a chunk.

Jason and Girondas watched. Herakles fended off with a long pole. Leonidas dipped up a chunk and some white stuff. "Cold," he said. "Very cold. Like snow on mountain tops." Ogg said he had heard of it as "muir-croinn," or "frozen sea."

Jason told the men to rest their oars. We stopped. Jason, Girondas, Ogg, and I stared about us at the prow. We were now surrounded. The cold, white stuff had closed around our stern. Only a low swell gave shape to anything. The white stuff rose and fell, and the gaulos rocked gently. Overhead the cloud seemed as thick as the sea. Often our mast-top disappeared.

We could not be sure of time. We thought it must still be forenoon, but the difference between day and night was small and we had only guessed at sun-up. Rifts showed this white sea stretching farther, now in every direction.

"A wind might blow it away," I suggested.

"Wind would hurt," Jason said. "Those chunks could knock a hole in the hull."

He turned to me.

"Pytheas, is this enough?"

If Thule was ahead, beyond this white stuff and the cloud, we had failed.

Or had we? No Greek, no Tartessan, no Maurusian, no Roman, no Persian, no Phoenician, certainly no Carthaginian, had been this far. Perhaps only the Aliones.

I found triumph overwhelming. This was indeed my moment. I was grateful to Apollo, Artemis, or whatever gods had watched over us, and I was most grateful to Jason and his men, now singing songs of home and girls at the quays.

Ogg and Herakles maintained a watch at the prow, each with a pole to fend off. I stood at the stern with Jason and Typhis. They watched the lookouts, I watched the straight path from our farthest north and west.

XVIII

THE COURSE BACK

I HAD SLEPT little in my excitement since leaving the Haemodae, so I lay on deck for a nap. When I awoke, we were sailing in a good breeze on open sea. The cloud had thinned and fleeting glows in the overcast showed us late afternoon sun, a beautiful sight, even though my own goal no longer was ahead.

Typhis was alone and easy at the steering oar. Jason lay near me. Many of the crew likewise, some asleep. When I sat up, Jason rose on an elbow. Girondas did not stir.

"You slept hard," Jason said. "We have sailed for hours."

"The last I saw was the fog. The last I heard was Herakles pushing away ice. Where are we?"

"Heading back for the Haemodae. Or so I hope."

"Will we go near those other islands?" I asked.

"Maybe. This wind has come up northeast and north. I do not know what that current is doing, except making too much chop."

The breeze held for two more days without clearing the sky. We wanted sun again. The chop often threw man-chilling spray. Jason, Ogg, and Girondas kept watch ahead. With the overcast, we had no cloud pillar to lead us to the islands.

However, sea birds told us we were close, and the long daylight saved us from approaching in darkness. Then the wind died and left a slop. We

---

The gaulos returns toward the Faeroes, fighting its way in a gale between Mykines and Vagar, Jason trying futilely to get into Vestmannasund, then sailing along Stremoy, finally bucking a strong tide to get into Sondini and a quiet bay, Tjörnevig. The men learn to eat sea-bird eggs and puffins. They are taken down the Sondini passage to Torshavn, and learn of tidal variations among the islands. The king also mentions Greenland beyond Iceland. The gaulos is piloted to sea and returns to the Shetlands, Ogg finding a harbor between the islands of Mainland and Yell.

rowed to keep steady and moving. In an hour or so the wind reversed to southwest, grew stronger, and we sailed again. The sky showed blue patches.

The next morning Eban, on lookout, called back and pointed ahead to left. Jason confirmed a landfall, but with anxiety. The wind was rising to a gale and visibility was poor.

"We'd better find shelter," Jason said. "And hope we are lucky." He headed us for the landfall.

Visibility got better as we approached the steep cliffs, white with bird droppings, of two of the western islands. The cliffs seemed to be layered horizontally with different kinds of rock. The closer we came, the higher the cliffs looked – as did the surf. More seals lay on rocks, some diving off after fish.

We thought we saw passages between and into the islands. We were sailing with a small island to our left and a larger one to our right. Jason headed us for the passage between. "Watch for any hole!" he shouted. Ogg was on lookout, knowing at least what to expect.

As we entered this passage, a strong tidal race seized the gaulos. The wind seemed doubled by the funneling of the cliffs – only twenty stadia apart at the narrowest. The cliffs themselves must have been more than a stadium high.

Luckily wind and tide went the same way. We sailed at frightening speed. Ogg pointed to what looked like a good harbor on our right, but Jason dared not risk the rips and overfalls tearing up the rock-guarded mouth.

We soon reached a headland of the bigger island and saw open ocean ahead. Jason, Typhis, and Herakles, Herakles alone at the weather steering oar, labored to turn us eastward to follow the shoreline, for the scant shelter of the island. The sea was quieter, but not much. Ogg sighted a bay but it was wide open to the north. Ahead we saw what looked like another harbor between this island and another, or just into this island. We sailed, no more easily, toward it. The wind often plunged from the cliffs, now two stadia or more high, in violent gusts. The gaulos jerked, swayed, and dipped. It pitched, rolled, and jumped. On Jason's shouts, the men rushed from side to side to balance.

Ogg signaled the helmsmen past scattered rocks and once around a whale. It took all their strength to force the gaulos to veer. I knew now that they had made the steering oars from Pasias' best timber. The shafts often bowed.

Jason and Ogg soon saw we would never get into that passage. They eased our course a little northward along this largest island. The great gusts smashed at us, and we continued at that awful speed. Jason had long ago taken in the mainsail and artemon, but the storm sail alone was often almost too much.

As we came to the northern headland of the big island, we again could see only ocean ahead. Land fell away to the east, with only distant islands dimly in sight. Jason had to make a hard choice – either let the gale sweep us on or try again for a harbor. Ogg shouted and pointed to our right. Jason rushed forward. There seemed to be a bay or a passage, with calmer water. Jason signaled to steer for it. I joined Typhis on his steering oar.

Jason quickly had the mainsail raised again for power and we could sail close in under the cliff. Ogg watched tossing swarms of sea birds for warning of gusts, and on his shouts, sail lines were slacked to ease pressure, then hauled tight again.

But as we neared the opening, we were struck by a great tide pouring out. It held us without forward movement amid leaping waves and overfalls. Jason saw we could not hope to sail in until the tide changed – who knew when? He ordered the already expectant men to their benches. All eight oars now gave us a little progress. Turbulence made smooth strokes impossible.

Jason rushed to help one older oarsman. I went to another, Leonidas to a third. Herakles had to stay with Typhis, and Ogg and Girondas at the prow. Eban manned his oar alone.

It may have been an hour, it may have been two. At last we got inside and found a quiet bay.

We anchored. The men pulled their oars aboard and furled the sails. All lay panting on deck. Gusts down the steep green slopes quickly dried sweat and we put back on clothes. The gusts swung the gaulos about her anchor, but could no longer harm her, even with the cove open at its seaward end. Looking out, we could see a white and tumultuous ocean.

"We were lucky," was all Jason could say.

It was late afternoon before we could stir. Ashore, on a small meadow, were stone huts. A stream flowed down higher slopes. Sheep grazed

Puffins were as strange to Pytheas as his ship was to them.

where there was grass, with two or three shepherds tending. As on the Haemodae, there were no trees, only low bushes.

A half dozen people ashore watched us – again, we hoped, with curiosity we could turn into friendship. Ogg, Girondas, Jason, and I went ashore.

Ogg was the one to talk for us. These people spoke nothing like any Keltoi we had found, but Ogg knew enough of their tongue to tell Girondas, who translated for us.

"They wonder that we got in here, he says," Girondas told us.

"So do we," Jason said.

"They welcome us. They see only voyagers from the Haemodae now and then. Once in a long while they see somebody from on east, that land that the king in the Haemodae spoke of."

"Do they know anything about my Thule?" I asked.

"They do not think anybody lives there," Girondas said after Ogg had asked. "Their fishermen have been near there but have seen only fiery mountains and boiling springs. They do not go ashore for fear of the fiery mountains that they have seen explode. But there are many fish there."

With this welcome, Jason let the men come ashore. Leonidas built a stone fireplace on the narrow beach, for Jason already had bought a sheep. The people also brought us sea birds and their eggs, a food we had not yet tried. One bird about as long as my foot had a blackish brown back and white breast and a huge red, yellow, and brown striped bill which could hold several fish. Leonidas dressed and roasted a few. They tasted of fish. The eggs also were stronger than any we had ever eaten.

"Ogg says they get much of their food from sea birds," Girondas reported. "They have to. They raise what they can from the soil and catch many fish, seals, sometimes a whale. But the birds are there always, with eggs in springtime. They nest in holes in the cliffs and on top, in rabbit holes or on bare ground."

Men and a few women gathered around us as we ate. They questioned Ogg and again he made a good story. He even sounded lyrical. I should teach him to write in Greek.

We offered Meton's wine. One man smelled it and handed back the cup, and the rest let him decide. Our wine supply was low by now, so we did not press it upon them.

Jason saw marks showing the tides must range at least six cubits here and told Girondas the gaulos ought to be beached to see if ice had damaged the hull. He decided to wait until we were ready to sail on back to the Haemodae. The men were weary.

Ogg and Girondas learned that the passage we had entered continued on between these two islands and opened on Okeanos at the southeast end. The people told them that at the other end was a bigger settlement, where their king lived.

"If we can sail through, it will save us trying to round the islands and all their rocks," Jason said. "We can beach there."

Ogg told Girondas following the passage would be easy. "In fact," Girondas laughed, "it will be so fast with the tide that we may have trouble stopping."

The next tide that could carry us there would be late at night, so we had to wait for the following afternoon. Girondas, Eban, and I climbed a high, table-top cliff for a noon observation. We were close to sixty-three degrees from the equator. So possibly we had reached sixty-five trying to get to the land of the fiery mountains, to my Thule, supposing that's what it was.

If my geometry was correct, we had come close to where daylight was continuous from equinox to equinox. Would the Aesymnète believe us? The Timuques, anybody on Our Sea? It was hard enough for me. Once more I wished for some way to know how far we had gone west. Five degrees, ten degrees? Again, how long was an east-west degree, here and at Massalia? How long would a straight line be from here to Massalia—across sea and land following the curve of our ball . . . as only a bird could go?

An older man offered to pilot us to the larger settlement. Ogg was glad. Our pilot and his son came aboard when the tide was about to turn the next day, and we towed their narrow boat with us. "How will they get back in that tiny shell?" I asked Girondas. He asked Ogg. The two men laughed and waved their hands back and forth. "They often make such trips."

We made the trip. Our men rowed all the way, not for speed, for the current carried us fast enough, but on advice of the pilots. "They tell Ogg it will be hard to steer unless we go faster than the current," Girondas told Jason. Jason and Typhis, using both steering oars, soon learned how to handle the gaulos here, and had the men on one side or the other make extra strong strokes to correct the gaulos' tendency to swing broadside.

Our pilots brought us into the lower harbor long before sunset. I gave them bracelets for their wives and obols for themselves.

"Ogg says they will keep the bracelets and make ear ornaments for their wives and daughters out of the coins," Girondas told us.

The men introduced us to the king and to their kin, who must have made up most of the settlement. Ogg retold our story and our visit turned festive.

"The king tells Ogg that if we had come in from the east they would have driven us off as invaders," Girondas reported.

"Tell him we tried to," Jason replied. "Those rocks out there are his fort."

The king laughed and made signs that there were ways past the rocks. These too were seafaring people.

Jason had Ogg ask about a place to beach the gaulos. The king shook his head.

"He tells Ogg you should have done it at the other end," Girondas said. "They have less than a cubit of tide here."

"So much up there and nothing here?" Jason asked. "Why?"

"He does not know. It's the way things are. He says that in a little bay on the east side of that next island there is almost no tide at all. I gather that's only about fifty stadia from where we were yesterday."

The water was too cold for the men to wade, swim, and dive for hull inspection, so Jason put it off until we reached the Haemodae. "I should know to do anything when I first think of it," he grumbled. "I hope wherever we land in the Haemodae the tides are the same as we saw." He recalled the range of five cubits in our harbor there.

The king and others told us again that the land of fiery mountains was to be avoided and that the ice really saved us from probable disaster. I still was sure that where there was livable land, people would live.

But the king told us also that men and boats from these islands at times sailed on west to another great, icy land beyond. "It seems to be made of ice," he told Ogg.

"Have they gone on to those fishing grounds the Alione told about?" I asked. "Have they seen Iberians?"

The king thought a few moments.

"He tells Ogg that men here have told of occasionally seeing strange, large ships in early summer," Girondas said. "They head south and west. The boats here never follow. There are enough fish in these waters."

The king went on in a longer explanation, which Ogg gave Girondas as telling of a boat once being driven by storms far down that coast to the west, landing among strange red-skinned savages who killed a few of the men, then finding its way back by way of the Haemodae.

"The men nearly starved," Girondas added.

As Girondas had said, "The sea stops nobody who wants to go – it takes him." Sometimes whether he wants to go or not.

"Are any of those men here now?" I asked.

The king shook his head. "It must have been many years ago," Girondas said. "They are all dead."

The red-skinned savages must be the ones the Alione captain had seen. Who were they? Was *their* land my Thule?

Jason and Ogg learned all they could on sailing back to the Haemodae–and on getting from this harbor to the open sea. Again, we had pilots offer to take us out, they to return in their own small boat.

We could get few stores, only another sheep and a few birds and fish. These could be eaten quickly, but there was no grain or other food to keep long. We were given a slab of a coarse, dried meat that Ogg said was from a whale. It was too tough and even Herakles, always ready to eat anything, had to spit it out of tired jaws.

"If you lived here, you would like it," Ogg laughed.

"I would have to be starving," Jason said.

Our pilots led us through the rocks, a less fearsome course than from the sea. The pilots dropped to their boat, raised sail, waved to us, and soon were dodging rocks easily.

"I still won't go in myself," Jason said.

We could see the waves crashing on the rocks and the surf flying high up the layered cliffs, even though the southwest wind was moderate. Birds followed us, but many more stayed behind, diving into the waves. We could see one big flock in a feeding frenzy over a school of fish. Seals harried any escaping. Aristotle wonders if fish sleep–they get little chance here!

Our return to the Haemodae was easy. The southwest wind held, the sky was clear, and the sea had only a small chop on the swells. We made our landfall, after Jason had corrected our course for the current pushing us northeasterly, south of the island we had first visited.

Jason's experiences during our first landing and later in the northwest islands made him less wary, and he let Ogg take us between two islands on the western side, and to a harbor at the southern end of the passage. The tidal currents were strong, though the range seemed to be only four or five cubits, and Ogg timed our movements to them. He knew the waters enough to keep us out of trouble. He suggested we ought to sail mostly at night, when we could follow a star, but Jason wanted to see more than a star!

That night we rested in calm water, Jason wakeful lest a falling tide leave us aground. I was wakeful too, watching strange stars. I felt satisfaction. Few men even had a chance at what I had achieved with, I knew well, the guidance and skill of the man beside me. I wondered if he thought back to our adventure with Tregela, Barda, and Rob. He had said nothing.

I broke the silence. "Do you suppose the caravan got them home all right?"

"Probably. Who is to know, though, unless we see ourselves? If we go that way."

He meant our destination was mine, not his. "It must be on our way," I reassured him.

"Maybe," he said. "Her realm is east of the cassiterite country you want to see. It's along a coast facing east, with some trade with Armorica. There's a smith-works where old bronze is recast. Even Wycomb's men carried bronze shields, not iron as on Our Sea now for a long time."

"I hope they used them only for pillows." The thought of a fight troubled him briefly.

"She says nothing was likely to happen," Jason added. "Of course they could have been waylaid in some lowlands with great forests she told of, or on moors, or at river crossings. But she and Barda and Wycomb's men knew the country enough. So did the traders. They were headed for a river to ship their elektron from. It's her harbor."

"Tregela told you a lot, didn't she?" I asked, smiling.

"That small woman was more than a pretty child. We talked while you and Simon saw the country."

"Did she say how Althos left things?" I asked. "I thought only men could rule."

"I didn't ask much. I gathered that as Wycomb said, Otho hoped to get her married to that Veneti, then get rid of Rob. That would have made him king. Tregela really must be queen only until Rob is old enough, the best I make of it."

He sat up and stared at the shore. "Until then, she is a lovely queen herself."

Jason wanted to say no more.

Meanwhile I kept thinking of the wonders of these lands and islands and waters to the north, and also those of all Pritania to the south and west . . . Albion's deep forests, barren moors, flowered glades, where people live in enough peace to be able to travel great distances with a few men and some shields piled in a cart. This is truly a mostly untroubled world, however fretful our own to the south and east.

Forests of Pritania such as Pytheas saw.

Even Otho's cupidity and the Veneti pirate's menace were trifling. I wanted to see more of the land. Its grains, its oats and millet and wheat, stored in pits, were delicious. I noticed that at Wycomb's hill-fort, food was stored within, perhaps against a raid by land or by sea. Yet in the village and about the farms nobody looked hungry, even deprived, so the hill-fort must have served all. Or so I hoped. And so hoped for whatever Tregela had from her father. Jason now saw her as no cute child but a queen, and I knew that Barda would see that she came to be what she must be until Rob was a man.

XIX

TO THE ELEKTRON SHORES

AGAIN, WHERE? We had to weigh the lure of the stone circles in the Orcades and on the western coast of Pritania against the Aesymnète's order about elektron and cassiterite. Jason kept time in mind. "The Dog Star's season – before you know it!"

The Cassiterides far to the south were on the way home, Abalus and other elektron lands on the mainland southeast. There we had to go. Jason beached the gaulos, inspected the hull, and found no work to be done.

Ogg met an old sailing man from Abalus who wanted to go home and knew the way. Jason took him on as pilot. We sailed to the eastern sea on a rushing ebb.

Our pilot thought six days should take us across. "He says the winds are mostly fair at this time," Girondas said after Ogg had talked with the pilot at length. "He also says there are currents to help us."

He had us sail due east a few hours to cross a northerly current, then south with another current that later curved east. We never saw the Orcades.

For all that sea's reputation for storms, we found summer winds light and variable. They kept us sailing, with no need to row but much sail trimming, and slow progress. The six days passed with no landfall. "He

---

An old Abalan pilots the gaulos across the North Sea to Stavanger, Norway, around Lindesnes into the Skaggerak and Kattegat, for a brief stop at Göteborg, Sweden, then into Lim Fjorden on the east coast of northern Denmark to Aalborg. The king tells of Samland (Prussia and Poland), to the east along the southern shore of the Gulf of Metuonis (the Baltic), and mentions the Hypanis (Bug River), the Borysthenes (Dnieper), Viadua (Oder), and Ister (Danube). The gaulos heads into the Baltic, through Store Belt and across the Kieler Bucht and the Mecklenburger Bucht, past the island of Rügen, and across Greifswalder Badden.

thinks the current is now taking us northward," Girondas reported. "He says no worry. On this course we come to land somewhere."

"What about those fierce people the island kings talked about?" Jason asked.

"He says they are that way only when raiding other lands. A few trinkets will keep them peaceful."

Sea birds again told us we were near land, and in two more days we sighted a rugged coast. It seemed sliced into deep passages between high lands, as if our Greek hero Herakles had hacked mountains with a sword.

Our pilot told us that elektron was found mostly in spring, washed out along beaches of Abalus or along shores of that gulf or inner sea beyond Abalus. That must be the Metuonis.

He headed us southerly against a slow current as soon as he was sure where we were. He pointed to a wide bay with islands and said a large settlement was inside. The entrance to the inner sea was two or three days' sail south and east.

In time we rounded the southern headland of this mountainous land. "He tells Ogg we are now in the crooked entrance to the inland sea and that it turns south around the northern tip of Abalus," Girondas said.

"I don't see Abalus," I said. "This must be wide."

"It is, and Abalus is almost all lowland. We won't see it until we get much closer, he says."

We sailed easterly and a little south for three more days before we sighted that northern tip. We felt we were on open sea most of the time, although we noticed a change in the sea motion when we left the deeps along that mountainous coast. Jason could not make out currents at the entrance. They seemed weak at most and at times dead. "Funny tides," he called them. But with light winds, some heading us, some helping, we slowly approached islands in the east. Our pilot said this was not Abalus but the land of the Gutones. I asked Jason to have him take us into a harbor he mentioned. We might find out something.

We went in among beautiful islands and anchored in a cove. Men who came out in skin boats spoke a strange, throaty language. If they knew anything about elektron, they would not tell our pilot. "As suspicious as the Veneti," Jason said.

The next morning our pilot took us southwest into an inlet on the east coast of Abalus. "He says this goes through to that open sea again," Girondas told us. "This northern tip of Abalus is an island."

We found a city of some size on the southern bank, with friendly people who spoke a Keltoi tongue. As Jason, Girondas, and I walked, we were hailed – and it was by the captain we had met on the Sequana River in Armorica. He made us welcome, and our men were glad to go ashore. The voyage from the Haemodae had been our longest, for them the dullest. As little as they wanted to be caught in storms, they liked excitement. A city had it.

Our friend showed us his raw elektron cargo. He was almost ready for his last voyage, since he too said elektron was found mostly in spring. From that I supposed that elektron somehow was a congealed sea substance, like the ice of our farthest reach.

I examined the pieces. Some had leaves, seeds, powder from flowers, bodies of insects or worms, or animal hair frozen in them. I had seen a little of this at home, never such variety. I wondered if the rich who prized elektron valued these inclusions or called them flaws. My brief talks with the rich had not covered such. Meton and Pasias would know, the Aesymnète certainly.

Our host introduced us to his king, who was proud of the way his Abalans lived. Jason mentioned our surly welcome across the water. The king laughed.

"What good things they have and know they get from us," he said. "We trade with them but they have to live a rougher life in a rougher land. Their life, and ours too, has been made harder by increasing cold. Our grandfathers tell of legends of much warmer times long ago, when we were even more prosperous."

He told us elektron often was so plentiful, washing out in storms on both eastern and western shores of Abalus, that low grades were used as fuel. "It burns nicely," he said.

My guess about elektron being congealed sea substance was wrong. It must be congealed from something on land, like the sap of a tree. It floated, and indeed it looked like waxy resin that oozed out of many evergreen trees. That burns well. This is beyond my knowledge. I can ask Aristotle. He tries to know everything.

The king was doubtful, as I had been, that Massaliot merchants should send ships this far for elektron.

"Our merchants will not send shiploads to you when they can sell it to the Veneti with short voyages, even though they would like to break the Veneti monopoly," he explained. "We do ship some around the northern tip of Pritania down to Belerion through the sea between Pritania and Ierné, but not as much. Also, the Teutoni and Balts who gather it on beaches on to the south and east and dig it out of the ground do all right sending it up their big rivers to near where your southern rivers rise. They certainly would not try the long sea route unless warfare blocked the rivers."

The Tanaïs, I thought. But he said "rivers." He knew there was no through waterway to the Euxine. He spoke of the Euxine, as we could not, until now, of the Metuonis.

"We get much elektron here," the king continued, "but one of the best sources is a place called Samland, land of the Balts, two weeks' sail south and east. It's also called Basileia. It is on land on the far side of a big bay where a big river flows in. That's the main river, with the Hypanis one of its branches, to start for the Euxine. Deep inland it is close to the Borysthenes that flows out of great marshes to the Euxine. Once in a while a Samland ship brings elektron here, but most goes up that river. There are other rivers. One, the Viadua between here and Samland, reaches back to near where a big one called Ister winds far to the east through mountain passes to the Euxine. They also can get to the upper Ister from that river through other mountain passes."

I wanted to see them all. "You will not live long enough," Jason laughed.

We asked the king how he had learned so much. "Traders pass along what they know."

"Carthaginians don't," Jason said.

"Who are they?" the king asked.

"You are lucky not to have to know."

Recalling how our travels had shown again and again that people everywhere traded widely, I was surprised that the king had not heard of Carthaginians. Yet, Girondas had often said they ventured only where profits were sure, quick, and rich. He had taken their ships as far as they had ever gone, well south of here.

In my spare Keltoi, I mentioned Massalia and told the king our city was Greek even though far from Greece.

"Greece," he said. "Here, I have something from Greece."

He showed us a vase with familiar markings. I was sure it had come from Mycenae, probably centuries ago.

"How did you get it?" I asked.

"An eastern trader brought it from the Euxine. They do have to bring back goods or they make no profit. I said they do all right, but the trips are not easy. There are river pirates. Or the traders may be caught in battles between Scyths and tribes on east. If they escape all that, the rivers may flood or go dry. We are happy to trade by sea. The sea can be terrible, but it does not prey on those who use it."

"We have pirates at sea, too," Jason said. "I know."

The king laughed. "We know, too, but the sea is big enough to give you a chance. You may be just out of sight of even the most bloodthirsty. On a river they know where to wait for you."

The Aesymnête had not exaggerated to the Timuques. No wonder elektron and cassiterite were dear.

Our host captain took Jason, Girondas, Eban, and me in a skin boat along the inlet to the western end, there to see the same sea that had brought us from the Haemodae. We sailed through narrow channels, past low green fields with scattered trees, then lakes with islands. We passed settlements where farming and stock-raising kept Abalans well provided for. Oxen pulled wooden plows, which our captain called "ards," in small fields inside stone walls. Horses drew two- and four-wheeled carts along roads, paved with cobblestones across frequent bogs.

"Straight west is Pritania," our captain told us when we looked out of the inlet. "Nine or ten days' sail with the right wind. It can be a hard trip. This is the widest part."

Sailing back Jason, Girondas, and Ogg questioned the captain on the route down the mainland to that narrow strait between Armorica and Kantion. He offered to lead us, but he was to leave soon and I wanted to go east, even to Samland.

As we neared the city, we saw boats moored along the banks or hauled out. The smaller ones were of skin, much like the one carrying us and those we had seen among the Veneti, with leather thongs and ropes drawing the framework together tightly. We went ashore at a shipyard, smaller than Pasias' but as busy, where a long, light craft was being repaired. Jason wondered how so narrow a boat, about forty cubits long but lighter than those on Our Sea, held up in open ocean.

No iron or bronze was used for fastening, but Jason saw that the hull was well built. Five edge-matched planks formed the smooth sides and bottom, each shaped well with an adz. Raised cleats with holes bored in them had been carved at intervals out of each plank across the grain. Cord through the holes fastened the planks to arched cross-struts and to

Trading ship from Norway under way.

each other. The seams were calked with resin. A sort of underwater ram stuck out at each end, curving upward above the waterline.

Girondas asked about the anchor chains he had seen holding larger boats on the Sequana.

"They have just started using them in the past few years," the captain said. "I tried to buy one once but they wouldn't sell it or tell me how to make one."

"Veneti, all right," Jason laughed.

Our captain and the head man told Jason and Girondas that the boat was mainly for sheltered water but could take considerable battering because it flexed with the waves. A dozen men with paddles could move it swiftly, with a helmsman at the steering oar.

As we came to the city quay, we saw a procession, headed by a decorated four-wheel, horse-drawn cart. The captain told us an elder who had died was to be cremated. He invited us to watch. Eban, Girondas, and I followed the procession with the captain.

Outside the city the cart was drawn up on a mound and the body, wrapped in robes, was laid on a rectangular bed of small logs, with pots and the elder's sword. Then a tent of saplings was erected over the bier. Straw and dry light wood underneath were set afire, and soon all was only hot ashes. A priest chanted and the elder's family wept.

"Burning the body lets the soul escape and the house over the body goes with him for shelter," the captain explained. "The pots have food for his journey and his sword will protect him against evil spirits."

He told us many persons had been cremated on the mound, which rose a little with each.

We walked back to the gaulos. Jason had rounded up his men. Herakles as usual carried two aboard after holding them head down in the water for a few seconds. Others soaked their own heads.

Our old man pilot from the Haemodae left us but Jason and Girondas felt we could find our own way east. "He says there are scores of islands and much sheltered water," Girondas said. "We will have to sail mostly by day, at least until we get into that gulf you call Metuonis."

We rowed out of the inlet at dawn and headed south along the coast. It was indeed easy sailing. The winds were westerly, off the low shore, moving us with little sea. There were night harbors enough, and after we had rounded one headland extending eastward, we began to see islands. There were other boats out, skin boats and some dug and shaped out of big logs. We hailed a few, but the sailors either did not understand Girondas' Keltoi or were unwilling to talk to us. We entered a strait about one hundred stadia wide, went through narrower waters, and came into a bay or sound. The pilot had told us to turn eastward here and to go between an offshore island and the mainland, then turn south again. "This should put us where the king said there was elektron trading," Girondas said. "He called the people Teutoni."

We stopped a night in a bay and tried to get more information. But the Teutoni, if that's what they were, were afraid that if they told us anything, they would be punished by Keltoi overlords inland. They urged us to go on east, to the mouth of the next big river.

"The Tanaïs, I hope," I said. "Maybe the Balts will be freer to talk."

Heat and a dead calm gave us cause to stay a few hours. I went ashore with Girondas and Eban. Eban had been turning the sand-glass since sun-up and at our noon sun-sight found the half day to be eight and a half hours, so the full day must be seventeen. We calculated the latitude at about fifty-four and a quarter degrees. I guessed we now must be at least ten and possibly twenty degrees east of Massalia. Such wide guessing did not rest well, but Jason still could not commit himself on distances in strange waters.

When we sailed again, we followed the coast northeasterly to an island. As we rounded its northern headland, we saw open sea ahead. We found a harbor in a bay, but people again waved us on east and south. We wondered if we were at the end of the Metuonis and on the western edge of a greater Okeanos – even the Erythraean Sea!

We coasted along the island's heavily wooded shores to the southeast. The light wind was mostly from the west, with little chop, and we sailed close to the beach, backed by sand dunes. We saw other small craft, some fishing, others hauling goods. After we had crossed the mouth of a bay, we were alone, still close in. The afternoon breeze died to leave us drifting in the heat. Jason had the men row for a half hour, then let them rest. Eban and I rowed ashore. I found shade and sat down. Eban walked half a stadium, then called. He pointed to something on the beach. I went to see. The object, half buried, was darker than the sand, what little of it was showing, and had a dull glisten.

I examined it. It looked like elektron. The boy was excited. Young eyes do see things. ("Young," I thought, "already his cheeks are dark with his first beard!")

We dug it out. It was a lump about the size of a lamb haunch. I rubbed a spot with a corner of my jacket, then held it to his arm. The hairs crackled. We took it to the gaulos.

Jason and his men crowded around. At the price it could command in Massalia, this lump might give all of us an extra reward. It seemed of good quality, with inclusions of leaves and insects of a time beyond even the memory of this country.

"How did the people here miss it?" I asked.

"Maybe some storm just washed it up," Jason said. "A local storm could stir up enough sea with nobody fifty stadia away knowing it."

That was good enough. I was beginning to question whether we should go on, and this at least paid us for coming this far.

An hour later, after a breeze got us sailing again, Herakles called and pointed ahead to an approaching boat. Jason wrapped the lump in sheepskin. "Lose it below," he told Leonidas.

The boat, something like the one in the shipyard in Abalus, hailed us. I thought pirates again, but Jason seemed unworried. He headed us into the breeze and a man came over in a small leather craft, paddled by two others. All looked determined but not fearsome.

He and Girondas talked in mixed Keltoi, with Jason adding an occasional word. The man seemed suspicious and Jason invited him aboard.

The leather boat stood off a few cubits, its crew watching us. They had daggers in their belts, as did the man who boarded our vessel.

Jason took him below and showed him our stores, spare sails, and rigging. When they returned to deck, Jason had a small amphora – to replay the game of the quay at Gadeira. Leonidas provided cups, and the man, like the Carthaginian officer, found Meton's wine good. Cup followed cup, and Leonidas called the men in the leather boat aboard. In an hour all was jolly. Herakles even poured his hoarded drink, and they liked that better.

Finally, a hail reminded our boarders of other duties and they returned, rings in the water marking missed strokes. We sailed on, our visitors the other way.

"May Artemis bless our wine," I said. 'Who were they?"

"Balts the king told us about," Girondas replied. "Somebody ashore saw you and Eban and rode a horse to tell them. One of their ports is not far. I told them you went after driftwood for charcoal."

"They believed that?"

"After the wine had worked a little."

"Wait till they find that Meton's wine and Herakles' stuff do not mix," Jason laughed. Leonidas pleaded not to do this again. "We have little wine left."

"The Veneti will sell us plenty when we get back down there," Jason said. "They make good wine and like staters. Where did you hide the elektron? I didn't see it."

"You won't be angry?"

"No."

Leonidas brought up the large jar the men used when weather made the rail uncomfortable. He took the lump out daintily.

"Tie a line around it and drag it overside," Jason said.

XX

A BUSINESS DEAL

WE SAILED ON, slowly. Soon we saw small boats moving in and out of a narrow inlet and guessed that must be the Viadua, the first river the Abalan king had mentioned. We headed in between heavily wooded banks, with Jason and Ogg watching ahead for shoals. Men on boats about us stared curiously and I suppose suspiciously. We rowed, with the wind failing completely, and found ourselves passing a shore settlement, then trying to find a channel through marshes. Stakes guided local boatmen, but we often guessed wrong and had to back off bars. Thousands of ducks and geese flew up before us. Everything was flat. Only scattered stands of trees broke the flatness. Small waterways made a wide and lonely labyrinth. With darkness, we anchored.

The next morning we came out on a large lake, crossed it, and entered the wide Viadua itself.

"This must be it," I said. "Maybe somebody will tell us how to get to the Ister and the Euxine."

"Don't count on it," Jason cautioned.

We came to a large town. As in Veneti ports, we saw sturdy river craft, with what must have been elektron cargos under mats and skins.

Girondas hailed a small boat to ask to go ashore. The boatman either did not understand or did not want to talk to us. Another was more

---

The gaulos is taken into the Oder, past Swinoujscie, across the Stettiner Haff, and to Szczecin or Stettin. The men learn of other rivers to the south, including the Vistula-Bug system. The men are given a feast, including meat from the now extinct auroch and from reindeer. With their cargo of amber, they return westward, sailing between Falsterbo, Sweden, and Klint, Denmark, through Oresund Strait, past København, back to Aalborg. The gaulos then follows Lim Fjorden to its North Sea exit, and is piloted along German and Dutch shores, through the Frisian Islands, past the delta mouth of the Rhine River and the Zuyder Zee, and back into the Seine River.

friendly, or more curious, and Girondas showed trinkets and told him we were only traders from the south.

"Tell him we want grain and meat," Jason said. "Tell him we will pay."

The man could see we carried no arms and the baubles were bright. He led us to a quay and took Girondas into town. Girondas returned with a roughly dressed soldier of rank. Jason again nodded to Leonidas for cups, and one of our last amphorae of wine was brought up. Leonidas was in despair.

Again Meton's diplomacy worked. Jason was able to buy food, and Girondas, with his ever quick mind for language, found information. The men he talked to were vague, whether intentionally he could not tell, about the rivers to the Euxine. Girondas gathered that it might take several weeks.

"Right now they can't get through," he told us. "All these loaded boats have been tied up for weeks. They've lost almost their whole season."

"Why?"

"Warfare. What the king of Abalus talked about. Several boats returned with their loads, some without, a few not at all. They're trying to find out if they can send them on to that next big river. But it and its tributary Hypanis flow through much the same country, so they may be closed too."

Once more the reason for the high price!

Girondas added, "They might be hungry enough here to sell you a little. Want me to see?"

Girondas made a deal to fill much of our hold. It cost us staters but Jason thought we might turn a profit. The trader was happy not to have to wait for the rivers to open, and I supposed we paid too much. After we had loaded, other traders approached us. We probably could have filled the gaulos until it sank, as light as elektron is. But I still hoped to add cassiterite at Belerion. Those knucklebone ingots would be heavy.

That evening our grateful trader took us all ashore for a meal in his big hall, almost a feast as at our stop at King Wycomb's hill-fort. Meat was plentiful, from a big ox-like animal and a smaller one with branched horns. So was the heavy grain drink. Jason had hoped to sail the next morning but soon saw that he, Girondas, Eban, and I likely would be the only ones to man the gaulos. We had left a disgusted Herakles to stand guard, but Jason sent Leonidas to relieve him halfway through the meal.

Herakles soon caught up on eating and drinking. Our host watched in awe.

When we returned in the thin darkness – nights still were short – we found Leonidas asleep and two strangers aboard. They fled. Leonidas was as remorseful as his aching head would allow. Eban and I had time for a noon sun sight and found ourselves about fifty-three degrees north of the equator.

As the men rowed toward the big lake, Jason asked, "Do you know enough about elektron?"

"Jason," I replied, "we have learned a lot, and we have seen a lot, and we have a load. Back to Abalus."

"Good," Jason said.

"Our host last night did say the shore east was much like here," Girondas added. "Then it turns north past desolate land."

"This is desolate enough for me," Jason said.

A westerly wind came up when we reached the big lake to let the men rest their arms and heads. We were soon among the marshes, trying to remember our way and spending as much time as before backing off bars. There seemed to be little tide, so the water did not drop from under us.

The wind was rising, and by the time we reached the lower settlement, it was a gale. "We better stay here a while," Jason said. "That sea probably can be mean."

We anchored and the men gratefully sought rest in the scant shade aboard. For all the wind, the sun was bright and the day hot. Those of us who were able went overboard to cool off in the water.

After the gale, a southwest breeze helped us along the shore of the big island northwest of the river mouth, and we soon came to open sea again. Remembering what the Abalan king and captain had told us, and adding what Girondas and Ogg had just picked up, Jason headed us northwest rather than try to work southwest into the wind. "There must be passages through all the islands they say are ahead," he said.

A short day's sail raised two headlands about fifty stadia apart. We headed more northerly up a strait between two islands with a town on the left. I would have liked to stop, but – time.

Two days more took us back to the Abalan city. We found our captain gone as expected, and called on the king. He was interested in the elektron problem at the Metuonis ports.

"This sounds like worse than usual," he said. "You and your trader were lucky to find each other."

"Maybe they will ship here if they can't go south," I said.

The king replied, "I will deal with them – at my price."

Girondas suggested sending an Abalan ship there, but the king said, "Let them come to us."

"We would just store it for next year," he explained. "If we took more to the Veneti now, they would beat the price down. They probably have heard what is going on in Samland."

"We will tell nothing," Jason promised.

"Good," the king said, "although the little birds in the air must tell them our secrets before we even think of them." Pasias and Meton would understand this talk well.

Grateful, he found us a pilot to the Sequana. "He can come home on our ship if it's still there," he said. He ordered the man to take care of us. "These are good friends," he told him. "You may sail one day to their city to trade." The king must have been rethinking his original reaction. I too began rethinking.

Our pilot led us out of the western end of the inlet but told us we would have to row south down the coast against a current – and the still southwesterly wind.

"Would we do better to head straight out to sea?" Jason asked.

"He says not," Girondas replied. "He says there's a big place out there where we might pick up a favorable current, but more likely we would be pushed north. This sea now seems to want to do that to us. When we were sailing north, it wanted us to go south. Anyway, he says try it his way for a day."

We did, with Jason holding the men to an easy pace in the heat. The pilot kept us close to the beaches. "He says the Cimbri live there," Girondas told us. Jason was nervous about being driven ashore if the wind rose. We coasted along until late in the day, when the pilot headed us more westerly after passing a low headland. About two hundred and fifty stadia out we found ourselves in a helpful slow southerly current.

"He says the water out here seems to go in a big circle," Girondas told us. "We can get help from it for a while."

Our pilot knew the coast well and now led us past shoals offshore and inshore. We passed the mouth of the Eridanus River which he said had some elektron trade. The coast now trended more to the east, along low islands. He found shelter behind one for a sudden storm and pointed inland to a wide, marshy, shallow bay.

"He says the people there talk about trying to close it off and drain it for farmland," Girondas reported. "He thinks the sea will beat down anything they try."

After the storm we sailed past long low beaches, and came to another big river delta with several mouths. "He says that river is swift back from the lowlands," Girondas said. "Big and swift. He does not think much elektron goes up. It flows out of high mountains."

The coast bent more westerly and Girondas felt we must be close to that dangerous narrow strait. The pilot nodded and we all kept a close watch on weather. We had to row much of the time, with wind against us and the current too half the time, but luckily the wind was light. We ran into patches of fog, though nothing like the night of Simon's rescue. The wind did reverse itself and get strong enough to push us through the strait, but against a tide for heavy chop that doused us with spray and often solid water until the tide changed. The men were glad to stop rowing.

"This heat is worse than in a notus off the Libyan desert," Jason complained.

Finally we entered the Sequana, after a wait for the big flood tide waves to roar upstream. We found our Abalan friend about to sail. He had sold his cargo at a good price, to his surprise. We told him what we had learned.

"The Veneti must know," he said. "The Balts compete with them in your markets and the Veneti likely were overjoyed."

I was glad I did not have to sell mathematics or astronomy by the cubit. Again, Pasias and Meton would understand. It was no news to Jason or Girondas.

They asked about anchor chains but the Veneti were evasive. "Veneti!" he grumbled.

Leonidas took money to find a vintner. Herakles and Ogg went with him and brought back filled skins and amphorae. Herakles carried only one amphora. I wondered why not the usual two. A smile under his beard showed he must have found the wine good.

"It may not be the Veneti's best," Leonidas said. "They keep that. But it is as good as we will find short of Gadeira or Syracuse."

"Or Massalia," I protested.

Herakles went below heavily, then called. Jason and I looked down. He had taken off his robe. Wrapped around his hairy chest and belly was a length of Veneti anchor chain. "Better than wine!" Jason exclaimed. Herakles let it down, covered it, dressed, and came up grinning.

Jason and Girondas tried to find a pilot to Belerion, but no one would admit knowing the way. Ogg finally thought he could do it. He had been past Kantion once to Belerion.

Our pilot joined the Abalan ship, with the captain glad.

"We lost two men in a storm," he told us. "It will be sad enough going home."

XXI

ALBION'S ATHENS

WE ROWED TO SEA the next morning with the Abalans and waved as they rounded northeast. We headed almost due north, with a southwest summer breeze.

"It will not be a long run," Ogg told us. "Keep watching."

"Just keep the fog away!" Jason said.

The air kept clear and before sunset we sighted land. An oak-prowed Veneti boat with leather sails that had started a little earlier stayed in sight all day and headed behind a big island. "That must be Vectis," Ogg said. "I always heard they shipped some white metal from there."

We followed the Veneti boat into busy water. We could see harbors, especially to the right, all with fishing craft. We followed up a wide river mouth and watched him tie up at a quay near the head. We anchored and soon curious fishermen and others came out. They understood our Keltoi enough, but told little about cassiterite. "The Veneti have them trained," Jason said, "or else this is not the real place."

It was good to be back in Albion. I was surprised. True, the fishermen

---

The gaulos crosses the English Channel to the Isle of Wight, called both Vectis and Mictis, up Southampton Water to anchor near Hythe, one of the Cinque Ports to be established in our eleventh century by William the Conqueror. Pytheas and Eban walk to the sacred spring where today's Winchester Cathedral stands, then across Keltoi fields to the Hampshire Avon River and Stonehenge. They may have passed the White Horse of Uffington or a similar phenomenon on some slope. They are brought back to a Channel harbor and the gaulos sails around St. Albans and Portland Bill, across Lyme Bay, and into the River Dart to Totnes and Tregela's hill-fort. Pytheas and Eban walk on to Todbury Castle and Tavistock, then to the tin mining and smelting country. They follow the River Hayle to St. Ives Bay on the northern shore to meet an Irish trader. They turn south again, passing the standing stone at Beersheba Leland and a stone fort, then follow a stream to Marazion at Mount's Bay, and go offshore to Ictis (St. Michael's Mount). They are in Pou Kernou, ancient Cornwall in Belerion.

told little. But I enjoyed the people, busy, productive, friendly, yet aloof.

With sight of the low green hills, my thoughts had slipped to where Jason's must be already—where to find Tregela.

He found a harbor, with a tavern ashore for travelers—and our men. We bought a mead drink. Girondas learned this was the land of the Durotriges. Pilgrims had come from the east, on their way to a temple inland. The mystery of the stone rings came back to me, and I asked to join the pilgrimage. This would slow finding Tregela's realm, part of the Durotrige land, but I had to see the great temple. I knew Jason would make his own inquiries while waiting.

Tired Girondas begged off and Jason stayed with the crew. Eban and I returned for an old sail to sleep on and food and wine, and we were off.

The pilgrims kept to themselves. They carried a votive offering for a plea to heal an ailing mother, their private matter not to be shared with aliens.

What beautiful country! We walked past small fields and along the edge of a great forest. To the east we could see the land rise. Part of our path lay along a stream, part over hills.

At the end of the day we had reached the temple. I was disappointed. No stone ring, it was a sacred spring with a small temple, surrounded by hills.

In my ever easier Keltoi, I asked if there were more, especially the great stone temple I thought I would see. A priestess showed a path to the west and described huge standing stones. After a night in a shelter for pilgrims, Eban and I went on westwards.

The air was good, even if no longer salty. The land was green. Small fields told of hard-working people. We were soon on a wide plain. I was not worried about getting lost. Our shadows told direction and paths were well beaten. Returning east and south, we would find our harbor and Jason.

Farmers and herdsmen were about. Farmers might return home from their rich grain fields, but herdsmen would stay with their animals.

By late afternoon we reached a river. Other travelers were there, but the ferryman would take no more across that day. I sensed uneasiness among the pilgrims—were we intruders? We were near the great temple. As the long shadows crept across the land, I began to see the heavy assemblage of stones in the sunset, still far ahead, but would strangers be forbidden to enter, even to see?

Pilgrims en route to the sacred spring, where Winchester Cathedral now stands.

We were tired enough to sleep where we were, but lightly. I did not want a knife to awaken me or close my eyes forever. Eban and I lay back to back.

When I awoke a well-robed stranger was sitting nearby. The atmosphere of the camp had changed. All now watched the man, and Eban and me, the real strangers. I shook away sleep and searched for Keltoi words. He smiled and raised his hand, offering us a bowl of water to wash our faces, then another to drink from. We took it on faith and found it a sweetish cereal drink.

Then we talked, slowly understanding each other.

He too was of the Durotriges, a chief or king like Althos, or priest. We were his guests. (I hoped not his prisoners.) He would show us the temple. Now the ferryman was respectful and obliging, but the pilgrims stayed behind.

Yet we were not to be taken into the temple. We only could view it from a distant slope. Black-robed priests seemed to be finishing a sun-up ceremony I wished I could have witnessed. I told my little king that I, too, studied sun and stars. This pleased him and I wished for Girondas to tell him more!

It was indeed a great temple, of such stones as I had not seen since visiting ancient Mycenae. Some were laid flat over uprights. There were two circles, the inner one of smaller, bluish stones. All seemed in a pattern suggesting use for watching the sun and moon, like the one on that farthest island in the Haemodae, but so much more complex. The array cast magnificent shadows—were the priests reading oracles from them?

But this was all we were to know. It was sacred. My king smiled away questions, mine or Eban's. Eban wanted to know most how the horizontal stones were put there. I was curious about the geometry and the possible astronomy. The king drew pictures on the ground and pointed, but told little that we could not see. We thanked him and turned to walk south past some herdsmen. But the king waved us to a small two-wheeled cart, again a little like ancient Persian war chariots, drawn by two small horses.

I had ridden little on wheels. It was grand to see the landscape fall away with no effort from my legs or Eban's. Thus do kings feel like kings, even bumping over stones. After an hour, the little ponies never flagging, we came to a hill-fort, much like the one at Deira. Not large, but the center of my host's kingdom.

We crossed a moat to a gate into the upright log wall, then walked to his dwelling. Dinner was being prepared.

But first we must see all his estate. He showed a threshing floor, roofed against rain like the one we first saw so far north, and a foundry where they made iron tips for their plows. These might also be for spears, but war seemed little part of their life. If this was all a stronghold, it wasn't strongly fortified. Farmers and herdsmen had easy access, as with Wycomb's.

The meal was wonderful. Meat, drink, bread, and fruit. I was expected to gorge, much as our Roman neighbors do, but my fill came before my host's. Eban did his share. Women sat at our table. I noted iron ormanents in their hair.

I wished for something for a gift, and finally gave the king my robe's bronze shoulder hook. He put it on his chest, like a medal.

On the morrow we again mounted the cart and headed south. In a surprisingly short time, the mast of our gaulos showed, and in another harbor. Our little king had sent a messenger to tell Jason to go to this other channel behind the island. Jason worried until he saw us.

We said our farewells, Girondas making them eloquent in his easy

Did Stonehenge look like this when seen by Pytheas, or was it still a beautiful Celtic temple?

way. I gave the king a small piece of our amber. It seemed out of place to offer him a trading trinket, or even a coin, although our coins were always well received.

Getting away depended on the tide, always in Jason's mind. As for myself, I had thinking to do. I had seen the land, visited a stronghold, and seen, at a distance, what must be the greatest temple in the land, at the hub of paths from all directions.

It had to be Albion's Athens! Strong kings must have ordered it built. It must have taken thousands of men. How did the great stones get on that plain? Who fed the workers? How could land be tilled or forests hunted if so many men labored thus? Over years–over centuries–kings and lordly warriors, priests and astronomers, poets, singers, common people, even slaves, must have come to worship, to study, to play. Gods like our Zeus must have joined, as on Olympus. I remembered the huge gnomon and the smaller stones in the land of the Veneti, just across the water we were sailing now, only an arm of Okeanos between. As Girondas knew, the sea joins more than it separates.

The fresh breeze was stimulating, and we were on our way to find Tregela's realm. We kept mostly in sight of land, rounding one point, then in the long dusk sought shelter before we came to a second. Next morning we rounded it and headed west across a bay, with Jason at the steering oar watching for landmarks he had learned from Tregela and Wycomb. The southwest wind crowded us landward. By noon we had low hills dead ahead, trending south, and soon Jason headed us into a river and a harbor a few stadia up.

We moored at a small quay with steps to the water. A few dugouts were about, but no large boats. Up the hill I could see two round towers on the crest. The quay area had several buildings, some dwellings, some shops for work or trade. Our strange ship brought people out.

Jason, Girondas, and I stepped ashore. The crew, furling sails and securing gear, looked about for the tavern that must be there. Jason ordered half, to their distress, to stay aboard until we were sure of ourselves.

We heard a horse trotting, wheels crunching gravel. A small chariot, decorated and colorful, came around the only corner. Tregela held the reins, Rob beside her. "Queens are supposed to have servants for that!" I thought. "This *is* a friendly realm."

"We've been watching since your ship came in sight!" she called. She was far from the frightened girl we had taken off a rocky islet to be one of our unwanted passengers. She hugged Girondas and hugged me—a heady experience for me even with my only thought for my own Anticlea, perhaps a heady experience for Girondas too. Jason she took by his hands, to hold for more seconds under smiling eyes than he counted.

We all talked at once, except Jason. I could not believe him to be bashful, yet he said nothing. Tregela beckoned Girondas and me to the chariot, and first held, then gave the reins to Rob. She spoke to her subjects gathering around us, told us the ship would be safe, and all were invited to the fort. She walked with Jason while Rob drove slowly ahead.

"Your sister . . . your queen . . . is lovely," I told Rob. He too no longer was a scared little boy.

"I guess girls are all right," he agreed. "Even queens."

The road wound up the hill, past small stone cottages with thatched roofs. On top was a wide embankment enclosing four or five square stadia. We went through a wooden gate and across ditches made when the embankment was built. Inside rose the two round gate towers, and beyond were round stone buildings, one quite large. There, as we might

A dress for Tregela.

have guessed, a feast was being laid out. Barda, ever regal, ever in charge, saw to servants and retainers getting ready, and greeted us.

"We meet more happily," she said.

"Talk later," Tregela said. "Let me show you our domain." Our sailors stayed behind, finding a shady spot. Barda had them served with cups of curmi. By the look in his eyes, Herakles clearly thought the cups were small.

Tregela led us about like a happy child. I had never known a woman so easy with people. In truth, though, I had never known a queen and in Massalia women mostly leave the world to men. Still, our goddess Artemis with her temples was friendly enough, and perhaps her spirit was in Tregela.

She showed us the covered storage pits for grain now ripening in the fields and the threshing shelters to keep it dry in the always moist air, even in the long sunny days of summer.

Cows and sheep and ponies were on the green hills. Tregela said that as in the lands we had explored so far north, the stock would be brought in for winter.

Hill-fort in Devon.

"Here is where we weave our wool and flax," she said, taking us into another stone building where women were carding wool and men were working looms. "But over here is what we make for trade, in our bronze works." I thought that for so young a queen, she knew already much that went with her office, and with Barda's guidance, would be able to deal with matters of state, commercial or political, as well as any man.

Her smithy showed us his products, pins for wooden wheels, wheel-rims, and fittings and decorations for harnesses, all cast or shaped in bronze. Our own bronzesmiths may do more intricate work, but none better. I agreed when Tregela exclaimed, "Aren't they beautiful?" Again, our Greeks had little reason to call anyone barbarian merely for being beyond our little world!

I asked Tregela where their bronze came from.

"Most of it is already made," she said. "Our traders buy it either new, or in worn or broken goods, like shields of warriors. They can be recast or reworked by our artisans. Some bronze comes from Armorica, some from our realms to the west."

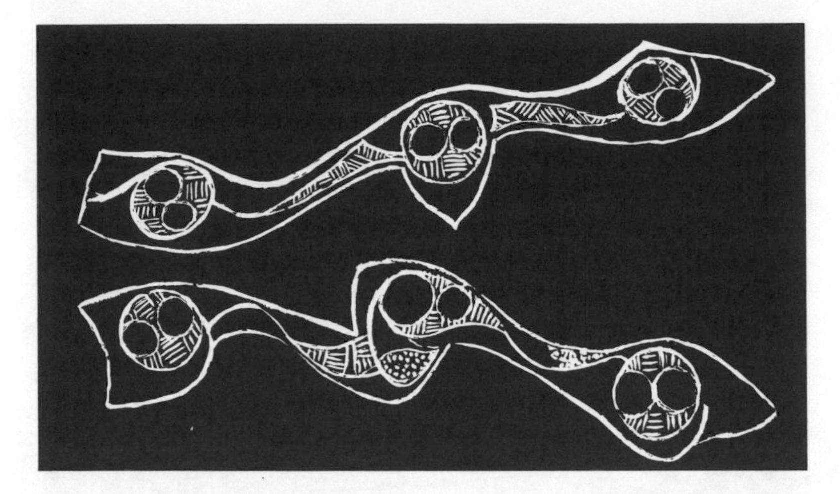

Engraved bronze Celtic harness decoration found in the mud of the Thames River.

"We want to go on there," I said. "We want cassiterite to melt with copper to make our bronze."

"Don't the Veneti sell it to you?" she asked.

"Yes, but our merchants would like to get it without paying the Veneti price."

"We have found no other way," she said. "My father tried."

"I'm beginning to think that, too."

We all examined fittings and decorations closely, and Tregela said the whole chariots, really carts much like the one she had ridden to meet us, were made near the quay by wainwrights whose fathers and grandfathers had taught them. "Almost everybody has a hand. The carts are small, for our winding roads and hills, but they serve well and our traders take some to Armorica, or as far north as Wycomb's realm. They bring back wines and cheeses and cloth and ornaments of that stuff you call elektron." I wondered where she had picked up our word for it; I had not mentioned our explorations in Abalus and the lands of the Balts.

I wanted to ask about Otho. He apparently had done much of this trading with the Veneti. Jason was silent, as he had been from the start of our tour, but Girondas was curious too. He asked Tregela carefully.

"Barda will tell you," she said. We asked no more.

Our tour went on to a tannery and harness shop, past small farms and their gardens, and back to the big hall in the hill-fort. As in Wycomb's Deira, I sensed little concern for invasion. Peaceful getting along must be the rule of life here.

In the great hall we were seated to the feast, Herakles gladdening the cooks by his great appetite, the rest of the crew taking their shares. Tregela must have guessed our thought that all was festive for a kingdom in mourning for Althos.

"My father taught us to honor our guests," she explained. "But for you . . ." she waved to all but looked at Jason.

Otho was not at the table. Barda, sitting next to Girondas, told him and me, "He is off with those traders who joined us."

We looked surprised, I more than Girondas.

"I told you. He is a charmer. He found time to make them believe he could be useful."

"But can he be trusted?" I asked.

"I doubt it, but their head man said he would see that he stayed with them, even back to their own land."

"But wine . . ."

"Their worst problem. Maybe they will make a man of him. We tried. Althos should have had him killed long ago."

"And if they don't?"

"We worry about that. If he gets back to that Veneti pirate, there will be real trouble. The pirate won't forget his soaking. And Otho won't forget how much he'd like to be king. That would be disaster. All we can do is hope. And be on guard."

Tregela welcomed, with a shy smile, my proposal for Eban and me to walk on to the cassiterite mines. Jason would stay, careen and refit the gaulos, then meet us at Ictis, the island where the Veneti got so much of their cassiterite. Jason said he wanted a few days to work, and I felt also to get to know Tregela, to overcome diffidence that must have been strange to him.

Tregela told us there were good trails and cart roads, and gave us names of hill-forts and castles to give all hospitality in the name of Althos. "They may not know yet what happened," she said. Our first castle stop would be in a port to the west across a wide peninsula, where her artisans received new bronze and scrap from Veneti, to be hauled overland.

An aerial view of the White Horse of Uffington, which was probably there when Pytheas visited.

"They will give you a feast," she promised. I thought we were feasting enough now for several days.

Eban and I set out the next day along a trail over the green hills, higher hills than those around the great stone temple. We found the castle, not so big or impressive as Tregela's but like hers in a hill-fort above a small harbor and settlement. We were well entertained and sent on an upland path to the northwest.

To our right was what looked like a wasteland, barren, boggy, forbidding, but with a herd of wild ponies and small flocks with shepherds. Our host had told us that every spring families gathered for a pony round-up, to pick the best and leave others with old animals turned out on the moor. He had given us a young man to be our guide. While three of us rather than two seemed no more protection on this lonely moor, I had little fear.

We spent that night at a crossroads shelter with harvesters on their way to reap and thresh somewhere. In the morning we turned west again, with the moor still on our right. We passed another small stone circle, then a walled village. Here our guide found us another to take us farther, and returned south and east.

Strangely, we seemed expected along the way. People were friendly. The land was hillier, fields smaller. Berries were ripening along the path, which often skirted forests but did not lead through. Skies were clear by day but in evenings great clouds piled up. We often joined herdsmen and shared food, and were shown sweet springs.

Again, I could hardly believe the beauty of the country. The hills reminded me of Greece, but greener. And there was so much space. I thought of our garden spot of Massalia and wondered if we could put a trading colony amid these hills, birds, flowers.

We met traders from the north going directly across the land to harbors on the south side. I wondered if they too hoped to bypass the Veneti, but learned little. Their language I had not heard, and they had come across that sea Girondas had mentioned between Pritania and Iernê. If they carried gold, as Girondas had said they might, they were in no mood to tell us.

They followed a river, and so did we, at a distance. Our guide said the river mouth was wide and sandy but ships could come a long way up past a headland guiding sailors in from the north. I wanted to see the mouth but our guide took us across a ford inland. We had passed mines, but I knew we were still far from Ictis, Jason, and the gaulos. There would be more, our guide assured us. We were now among tribes of Dumnonii, he said, with several kingdoms rich in cassiterite.

Celtic food bowls.

Celtic fields such as Pytheas might have seen.

We spent six days on the road, over hills, through dales. By the third night we were in another kingdom, and, I gathered, the land of cassiterite. We were taken less as strangers, more as traders, and traders were welcome. Here and there we met men who understood our limited Keltoi. Strangers had walked these ways before. When? The Cassiterides had drawn men for centuries.

One day we saw men working at a stone furnace built almost like a small castle. Some ground lumps of black rock between flat stones, turning the upper stone by hand. Another man tended the charcoal chamber of the furnace. The best we could see was that the ground black rock was spread on charcoal, with layers of charcoal and ground rock alternating.

Nearby others beat recently smelted gray, white-spotted metal into big flat lumps. Two ingots, shaped with four long ears from a central mass like an oxhide, were being loaded on a cart.

I had seen such shapes at an armory at Massalia. Now I knew what cassiterite was made from. Next I had to know where the black rock came from. Soon we saw.

The paths now were wide, for big carts. Farther along we saw on a hillside what looked like a fan-shaped stream of black widening down the slope, and wider on the low ground. There was the black rock! It looked as if it had flowed out of the hillside, as it might have in some past great flood. Men threw small pieces into a cart. Bigger pieces were pried free with picks made of horns of a large animal, or with bronze or iron axes. The pieces had to be broken up and the men placed them on boulders to pound with hard rocks. The boulders had depressions worn in their upper surfaces. It was hard work and I hoped the men were not slaves. They worked with more gusto, I thought.

At another digging, broken black rock was thrown into a log waterway from an upland brook.

A sluice. The flow washed away dirt but left rocks and heavy black sand. The water was stopped by pulling out a log, and the rocks were loaded on a cart, the sand into wicker baskets. I supposed the sand could be put right into a furnace, while the larger pieces had to be pounded fine, as we had seen.

The overseer saw our interest, and gestured to tell that such diggings were scattered over the countryside, some bigger, some smaller. We later saw one with a shaft, like mines around Illipla but not deep, another where the rocks were picked from a stream.

We came to a river flowing north, with a heavy cart trail beside. We followed the river until it widened into a harbor, speckled with sandbars. Boats there were round and hide-covered, like the Veneti's. One at a quay was loading cassiterite ingots over brush protecting the bottom. These must be sailing north. To Ierné?

I tried my Keltoi on a red-bearded man directing loading. If he understood, he gave no sign. Eban looked at me and stepped forward. He offered a few words that sounded almost like Girondas', and smiled earnestly. The red-beard responded indulgently. Respectfully, Eban asked where he was taking the load. The answer was Ierné.

Then Ierné was a separate land, as Girondas thought.

He made Ierné sound as big as Albion. Beyond it lay Okeanos, with storms from where no man had sailed. I was reminded of sailor-talk we had heard when we turned back short of Thule.

The red-beard and Eban talked on, Eban asking how they paid for the ingots. The man answered, "Gold." That told us the value of his cargo. Then he talked about his Ierné again, a beautiful country, but with much fighting. He was glad to get away occasionally. So we had something in common! I would tell Meton and Pasias that here was another place for a colony!

He talked more of gold. He even showed a small clay jar of nuggets he said he hoped to sell himself, and not for cassiterite. Eban looked wistful. I had one of Philip's gold staters to offer and the Ierné captain turned to me and held up his biggest nugget. I was quickly happy with a piece of beautiful gold, he with a stamped golden coin he had never seen. We parted, we still to find Ictis after this detour. The red-beard thought it was south a day's walk. He had never been there.

Along the path we passed a single standing stone, straight as a young sapling. A farmer told us it was called Longstone, but what it marked he did not know.

There was a fort at the top of the hill, with stones laid to continue the lines of natural outcrops. It looked impregnable, but no sentries were about, so again apparently no invaders were expected. Later I learned that it was only one of several in the neighborhood, the largest and most elegant called Chûn.

The next river we found flowed southeasterly. It led us to a town and bay. There lay the gaulos, safe in the marshy mouth. We looked for Jason and all, then saw the little island, offshore four or five stadia.

We had arrived! We had let our guide return home, with a handful of obols. Now Eban and I were alone. We sat on the ground to rest before going on to meet Jason, Girondas, and our gaulos.

I thought back to Tregela's snug realm, its harbor and hill-fort, and Jason. Would it be part of his life? He knew she had stepped into his life and he into hers. It was a new experience, one that had him, of all men, confused.

I could see why. Sea captains, even owning their own ships as he will when we return to Massalia, are still thought of more as artisans than men of substance. I knew of no sea captain among the Timuques. It might not be enough that I could call Jason one of the finest men I had known—fearless but cautious, autocratic on his ship but considerate, strong but gentle.

Tregela was a queen, tiny, lovely, gracious, and capable. Her regency might end with Rob's manhood, but perhaps not. Whatever, that was years ahead. If not of her own realm, she might be queen for another king of Albion. Neighboring princelings must be thinking of that. Barda or her grandfather might already be casting about, although I felt that Barda had found a single life good and could help Tregela do likewise. And Tregela, I knew, would have her own mind.

All I could be sure of was that Tregela would never forget Jason if she let him go. And, he could have a way with women that I hadn't seen in his seemingly monastic shipboard life, and even now be promising to return to her realm.

All I could be was Pytheas, who had seen where day ends in day in summer, who had found Pritania to be a large island, with an almost unknown Ierné across a sea to the west, and beyond that Okeanos stretching how many thousands of stadia, even beyond Thule, to that other rocky coast an Alione captain knew and whatever is beyond that land. I had seen tides rise and fall nearly twenty cubits and I had seen dew so heavy that rain almost seemed not needed for growing things. I had found men living close under Arktos, raising food or getting it from the sea, and unaware of the warm lands of Our Sea.

Indeed, a bigger world than any of us, even Aristotle, had imagined.

Eban was quiet beside me. I asked him what he was thinking.

"How much farther and have we anything left to eat?"

Thus philosophy!

Ictis! And what a jewel island—a cone, studded with rooftops, rising from water. A Veneti ship moved out with the ebb. Later, as the tide fell, empty wagons rolled from the island to the mainland on a drying causeway.

I was too tired to try the causeway. There would be another low tide in the morning. We walked down to the edge of the bay to rejoin our ship and our Tartessans.

With the next low tide, Eban, Girondas, Jason, and I were ready to walk the muddy causeway. Jason again had awaited us anxiously, not knowing what might have happened on our land exploration. He rarely went far inland from any shore.

A chain stretched across the roadway, a guardhouse beyond. Two loaded carts awaited the tide.

At last all the causeway showed. A guard appeared at the chain, and behind us another cart stopped. A well-dressed man stepped down, and the first carters were admitted to the drying road. The man invited me to ride on his cart. He knew we were from the gaulos and spoke as one merchant to another, even though we had few words in common. He might be talking to someone offering more than the Veneti for his two loads of cassiterite.

I was glad to keep my feet dry. My companions from the gaulos used

The Ictis of Pytheas' time, now St. Michael's Mount, in Mount's Bay, Cornwall.

staffs in the slippery footing. Once across, my new friend introduced me to another man, apparently his partner, then followed his wagons.

Mount Ictis was beautiful. A small farm lay at the bottom of the hill back of the storage shed where my driver took his ingots. Two paths were before us, one around the shore, one up through trees and past small villas. These must be homes of merchants.

Ah, to be fluent! My host seemed to know that I was not a buyer, but possibly an advance agent. Meanwhile Girondas, Eban, and Jason arrived and cleaned their sandals in a pool. We all took the upward path.

With Girondas able to talk easily, we learned that this country was Pou Kernou. The lower villas were homes of cassiterite buyers. Traders who bought what the Veneti brought lived on the second level. The highest villas were most elegant, but little explained. Girondas thought they might be where the gold from Ierné found its way, and elektron from the Abalans and even Balts. We were shown a beautiful gold-and-elektron necklace, fit for a Tregela, the price beyond us.

From the heights we could see several mines in hills of the mainland, and more beautiful homes, possibly the castle from which my first friend had come.

Jason's and Girondas' minds were on the rise and fall of the tide. Beautiful as everything was, we did not want to be prisoners for twelve hours. We went down to the first level and found our host had ordered a great meal. As we ate, we talked, Girondas supplying phrases and words. Pou Kernou would welcome merchants from Massalia. They had not really liked Phoenicians in their time nor Carthaginians later. Tartessans were only a memory. (Jason tried a few words in Tartessan but no one understood.) Greeks they might have known, but if so they too were a dim memory.

I saw empty carts starting back. My first friend joined us, and shortly he rose and invited me to follow. We all walked to the quay together and he explained that if the others waited an hour, a little boat would ferry them across. We did not like to be separated, but neither did we want to offend our hosts.

No foreign ships were in the harbor, but I thought I saw a sail in the offing. We would soon be across and out of sight, if Veneti.

I waited for my shipmates in a tavern at the end of the causeway. Such bustle and urbanity I had not seen since Massalia.

This was a second great moment in our voyage. I had learned more for Massalia than the Aesymnète had asked. I myself could absorb no more geographic wonders. I would ask Jason to enter no more strange harbors, seek no more strange landfalls, no more mysterious stones.

We would race the equinox home.

XXII

HOMEWARD

NOW I COULD LOOK HOME—to my Anticlea, Dryas, and Anthia (I had no playtoy for her yet!). My shipmates no longer had their old homes, but I sensed glad expectation of familiar seas.

Jason still was almost aloof, offering no confidences. I could only guess what kind of farewells he and Tregela had said.

Girondas alone seemed unmoved. He knew as we did that he could expect to see few new seas and shores. How few only his Sun God could tell.

We had three weeks to equinox. Jason was impatient. "We could catch plenty of trouble right now." Days were shorter, the mornings often crisp, the sun farther south.

Jason had had needed work done on the gaulos. He had loaded aboard food. The merchant partners had let us have four ingots of cassiterite and several sizable pieces of black rock. A wagon brought them to us at night. No Veneti ships were in port, but the men did not want our purchase widely known. We paid in staters and I hoped some money would go to the men who mined and smelted the metal. Jason laughed. I did pass a few obols to the wagon driver.

Jason looked at our loaded waterline and told us we must get by Gadeira and the Pillars of Herakles without stopping. "If the Carthaginians see cassiterite and elektron, they'll go wild."

"This is a Massaliot ship," I protested. "It's none of their business!"

"If there's money, they make it their business."

"It'll be piracy!"

"You Greeks can make piracy illegal, but you can't make it unpopular. The Maurusians don't see anything wrong."

"You mean we'll be smugglers!"

"Who isn't a smuggler some time?" Jason was merry. "He's just a sailor bringing what somebody will pay well for, and getting it past somebody else. It's no crime, it's a game."

We went out on an ebbing tide and a light land breeze. As at other long stops, our crew left sad-eyed women on the quay. Herakles brought aboard an amphora of the local grain drink.

"He found out how to brew it," Leonidas told us. "Your vintners are going to have competition."

I wondered how Herakles' Tartessan questions could have drawn the recipe from men speaking only their kind of Keltoi. "When he wants to know something," Leonidas said, "he finds a way. He watched them make a batch. His first will wither grass."

I reflected that bringing brewing to Massalia might be more important than whatever cosmic knowledge I had gained.

"Don't let that surprise you," Girondas smiled.

Jason headed us south, and with the wind westerly we sailed as fast as our load would let us. He and Girondas worked out a course to touch at northwestern Iberia, perhaps at the harbor where we replaced the split planks. (I hoped we would find the Alione captain. I would like to tell him about the storm-driven islanders we had heard about.) Girondas remembered a current that would help us. Neither he nor Jason wanted to be pushed into the Oestrymnian Gulf. There equinoctial storms could be even worse than on Okeanos. We would pass close to Uexisamé, then head for Iberia.

We had a faster crossing than Jason expected. The wind held steady and strong enough. As low as we were in the water, we often took a wavetop aboard, but the gaulos was under no strain. After passing Uexisamé, we had to head a little more into the wind. We sailed more slowly, with pounding.

The air was clear, the horizon sharp. Stadium after stadium we sailed. Jason watched sun by day, stars by night, and our wake always. Eban and I joined the star watch. During the day Eban was busy as a sailor, and I wrote my journal and refined my map. All would go into our Library at the Hall of the Timuques. I hoped all would be copied and sent to that new library at Alexandria, if Alexander's satrap Ptolemy had actually established it. Another copy should go to Aristotle for his Lyceum at Athens. Thus perhaps everybody's knowledge of the world would grow a little – if my story were believed!

Shipboard life fell into the unchanging ways of sailors. Typhis, Ogg, and Jason spelled each other at steering. Ogg had, as I expected from his adventurous nature and his curiosity about Our Sea, stayed with us. "Maybe Jason will take me home in another year," he said. "Or maybe I will never go home."

"Don't you have family?" I asked.

"Kin, nothing more. My father was lost at sea, my mother died of grief. Simon knew I wanted to go away."

I awoke on our fourth morning to see Jason kneeling by Girondas.

"He is dead," Jason said. The men gathered. "He did not wake up."

"So close to home," I said.

"Let us not be sad. I knew this would come when he joined us at the well. I knew also that neither he nor I could do anything about it. He died where he wanted to die. He has gone to whatever our Sun God holds for free men, and as a happy man."

I recalled Girondas' refusals to join our last shore explorations. He must have sensed death. Yet he was cheerful, helpful, and alert. Only last night he had told us at supper of young adventures, as a galley slave for Carthaginians at Gadeira, then as a more valued property, a man who could navigate so much better than their own captains.

Now all he knew had been passed on to Jason. Jason would pass it to Eban. Much I had put in my journal, but no journal could tell Girondas' ways, his ease with strangers, his gift of language.

Jason alone prepared Girondas for the sea. He wrapped the spare old body, the tiny Attic lamp in the arms to light the way, in sailcloth and sewed it tightly. He weighted it with ballast. Typhis brought the gaulos into the wind. Jason lifted the body in his arms and carried it to the rail. One last embrace, and Girondas sank in a wave.

Jason nodded to Typhis. The gaulos was put back on course.

XXIII

THE PILLARS AGAIN

IN ANOTHER DAY we raised the Iberian headland but Jason said, "We are making good time and we need every good day." I forgot about the Alione. No one in Massalia would believe him, anyway.

Jason kept us well offshore. We still had a helpful current and a westerly wind, but Jason knew that the good weather could not last and he did not want to be caught close in by a gale.

The wind instead first turned fitful and Jason watched clouds and sea closely. Then a gale did come, out of the north. Blowing with the current, it did not build huge seas, but enough.

On toward the Sacred Capes we rushed. Jason took off the main and artemon and put on the little storm sail, then took it off too and towed all our heavy line.

"I told you storms come when they please," he shouted.

He seemed to enjoy the gale. Perhaps it eased grief. Yet he was ever watchful for the ship and men. He saw to it that all not called upon to move kept lashed to the mast or rigging. On night watches Ogg and Eban shared the bow lookout.

There was no fog but spray was thick and we could see little past the back of the wave that lifted us, rushed under hissing, and left us in the deep trough. Herakles and Typhis or Jason manned both steering oars—Herakles refusing to rest when his great strength was needed. Again and again the steering oars were bowed but always came back to true. I blessed Pasias' best timber anew.

The gaulos returns to the Pillars of Herakles, first sighting the Atlas Mountains of Africa, then being stopped in the Strait of Gibraltar. In its flight from pursuing Carthaginians, the gaulos is caught in an argestes, the Mediterranean's cold northwesterly gale, the mistral.

Leonidas often went below. We heard, even above the roar of the wind and seas, groaning of our timbers and knew that the gaulos' hull was flexing to great stresses. If the papyrus tow and other calking worked out, Jason wanted to know quickly. I wondered what he could do about it, then remembered how many other storms he had been in. Only fleetingly did one remark come to me – "There's always one that's your last storm."

The storm lasted three days. When the wind died to a southwesterly breeze, we bounced on a lumpy sea for a day. Jason could not tell how far we had been blown, so he headed us easterly. "We may be past the Sacred Capes," he said. "If so, Libya is what we will see first."

"Libya and its Maurusian pirates?" I asked.

"Hope they're busy somewhere else."

When we did raise land – at first the peaks of a range of mountains – it was Libya. Jason headed us northeasterly, well offshore. "This will take longer," he said, "but clear of Gadeira."

He knew these waters and spent much waking time – he now could catch up on sleep – explaining piloting problems to Ogg and Eban. "We will slow down after a while," he said, "so we can pass both Gadeira and the Pillars at night. Hope for clouds. We have too much moon."

We never saw Gadeira. Jason moved closer to the Libyan coast with darkness, then had the men row in the light breeze.

"Okeanos flowing in will help us," he said, "if we just aren't seen. Let's have luck again."

We had clouds but no solid cover. The half moon broke through often. Our sail had weathered gray yet seemed to shine. Jason took it down as we approached Abyla and Kalpé. The men rowed quietly. Nobody spoke. Jason gave commands almost in whispers.

He turned to Typhis and said, "Remember – keep clear of that outcrop and long ledge." I saw no outcrop and told Jason. "It's there," he said. "I know this strait – night or day." He pointed off the bow, toward the Libyan shore. I still saw nothing!

We were well into the strait when Eban came aft to report a ship ahead. Jason went forward. I went too, curious and excited. Were we to be stopped now, so near the end?

The ship was coming out of Herakleia, the Carthaginian base in the shadow of Kalpé. Jason stopped the oars. We drifted.

The ship, a large one, was headed west, probably for Gadeira. It would be under oars against wind and current. Jason signaled for the men to row again. Typhis edged us more toward the Libyan shore. We eased quietly away and had gained a stadium when we were hailed.

"Who are you?" came in Carthaginian.

Jason shouted a name from his imagination. "Grain and copper from Onuba for Carthage," he called.

"Come alongside. We do not know you."

The ship had been stopped by her oars. A score or more men stood at her rail. Some held spears. Both craft drifted slowly eastward with the current and breeze. We drifted a little faster for having been underway.

"Come close," the Carthaginian ordered.

A longboat was lowered. We could see eight men. That probably meant four to board us, four to handle the boat. Jason had the oars backed to stop us, but watched toward the Libyan shore, possibly twenty stadia south.

Our fate could only be capture, imprisonment, and robbery. No wine would get us out of this. I rolled together journal and maps and strapped the package inside my jacket. I tied our money pouch on me. I might have to learn to bribe. I had to get journal and maps to Massalia. Philip of Macedon is supposed to have said, "A donkey laden with gold can scale the steepest fortress."

Jason as usual showed no worry. I took a little comfort knowing he had dealt with Carthaginians. He had said something rapidly in Tartessan to the crew, who nodded without speaking. When the longboat came, he helped the four men aboard. If they recognized him or he them, there was no sign.

They were grim. Their boat was ordered to stand by. Jason offered a rope, but the boarders refused to tie to the gaulos.

Jason led a gray-haired officer below. The others stayed on deck, spears and swords at the ready. We could hear Jason and the officer talking, with stern questions, pleasant answers. With what Carthaginian I knew, I gathered that Jason was naming names in Onuba.

He then explained, with enough truth for plausibility, that Maurusian pirates had destroyed his ship, belonging to an Onuba merchant, and that he had gotten the gaulos from the Greeks at Massalia. Then I heard him tell of our fight with the pirates and delivery of the captain's body and freed slaves to Gadeira.

The Carthaginian grew hostile. I made out his scornful "So you say."

Then I heard him rummage through the cargo, and a stern "What is this? Where did you get it?"

Jason replied in Carthaginian but was shouted down, "Tartessan slave, you stole it!"

Jason called out in Tartessan–what his men were waiting for. They exploded before the three guards could move. Herakles grabbed two guards in his mighty arms. Eban dived to the third's knees and threw him. Two others pinned him. The officer's head came up through the hatch. He was struggling either to drag Jason up or shake him off. Someone kicked the officer's bronze helmet off and the heavy hatch cover down. Herakles shifted his captives into one arm, wrested away swords and spears with his free hand, threw the men over the rail, and handed the weapons to fellow crewmen. Then he pulled up the third guard from entangled arms and threw him overside.

The sailors in the longboat rowed up in a rush, but Herakles reached over the rail and twisted the stem until the craft capsized.

The hatch opened and Jason dragged up the officer, limp and unconscious, his scalp bleeding. Herakles threw him after the rest. The Carthaginians clinging to the overturned longboat grabbed the now reviving officer and shouted for help.

I looked astern. The ship was swinging slowly, left oars backing, right pulling, to head for us. Scores of men were at the rail with spears. Archers were in the mast-tops. The captain shouted angry orders.

Jason too shouted and quickly we were under way, all eight oars strong. We gained our speed and put several stadia between us and the ship before it could move forward. I was grateful for inertia.

Jason stood in front of Typhis, looked to our right toward the south-trending Libyan shore, and held his arms pointing to two widely separated humps. As we moved parallel to the shore, Typhis steering carefully, Jason closed the angle between his arms. Now I saw that outcrop ashore!

The ship was gaining, as even I knew it must. I could see the oarmaster's long whip slashing in the moonlight and hear the slave rowers' screams of pain.

Jason watched his marks. He put Typhis into a wide curve, seemingly trying to dodge–for all I could see, heading for the outcrop. Even with my faith in Jason, I was frightened.

The ship followed. Our lead shrank to the range of a well-thrown spear. One missed Typhis by a half cubit and stuck in the deck.

I could only think, the end. The Carthaginians held their arrows, hoping to take us alive for slaves. I thought of swimming to shore with my precious package. But Jason and the men would fight, and so must I.

Jason dropped his arms and Typhis straightened our course, parallel to the shore and outcrop. Spears fell closer. One hit a crewman's arm, opening a wide gash. He dropped that arm but kept on pulling. I rushed to stop spurting blood the best I could, and wrapped the arm with my jacket. Jason sent Leonidas to help him. I went to the oar, hoping to maintain rhythm.

Then I heard Jason.

"It's all over."

Jason surrendering?

Typhis held the steering oar lightly while watching astern. Jason went to the poop rail, and the men all stood to watch.

The ship had stopped. The deck was canted. The masts tilted forward. Tangled, broken rigging hung down. Cursing men were in the water. Slaves jumped overboard to try to swim the eight or ten stadia to shore.

"What happened?" I asked, leaving my now idle oar to join Jason and Typhis.

"The ledge. If he'd been through here as many times as I have, he'd know too."

"But we . . . ?"

"We draw three cubits loaded, he draws six. The rock has four over it."

The men returned to their benches. I offered to take the wounded man's oar. He was sitting in pain, with his arm bound. Leonidas had twisted a cord around the arm and loosened it every few minutes until the blood in the cut and bandage thickened.

"I need the exercise," Jason said.

He took the oar. He gave Typhis a course east through the Sardoö Pelago toward the Balearico and we got under way. I went forward to watch for other rocks, hoping to be useful. We rowed until daybreak. A brisk westerly zephyrus came up with the sun and the men rested, half of them asleep.

But not Jason.

"Watch astern," he warned. "They must have sent back for help. A yawlboat could make it in two or three hours. They'll be after us."

Jason changed course often. "I hope they think we'll make it easy," he said.

Noon passed and we still had only a horizon astern. Jason slept, but Typhis, Ogg, and Herakles watched there, and forward as well for pirates prowling. Eban climbed the ladder to the masthead and looped a length of rope for a swinging seat.

Two full days passed. I felt relaxed. I asked Jason if we were still in danger.

"They want revenge."

In a moment when we could think of other things, I mentioned that I had forgotten gifts for my family. "They will have to forgive me again." Jason only shrugged. Later he offered me a bundle and asked, "Will these help?"

Inside were a small gold brooch, a bronze hand-axe, and a vase with a strange design in gay colors.

"How beautiful!" I exclaimed. "I didn't know you were trading."

"I kept in practice. While you and Eban explored Belerion, Girondas and I did a little."

"I should have. I always forget."

"Well, take these."

They were no peddler's trinkets. Had he picked them as gifts for Tregela? Had she not accepted them, or him? Or were they for someone on Our Sea? Or had he others in the hold to sell in Massalia?

"Will they do?" he asked.

"They are perfect. But you can't just give them – let me pay you. They . . . you have saved me."

He smiled and shook his head. I laid them on the deck. The brooch had the gold lunilae design of Ierné, borrowed by some artists on Our Sea. I knew Anticlea would prize it, perhaps forget long months. Dryas often had asked for a hand-axe and I had held off, to protect growing shrubs if not his own fingers. He was old enough now. Whether Anthia fancied a doll rather than a vase I would know soon.

Jason's gift emboldened me to probe beyond my affairs.

"If you go trading, Jason, do you think you might ship . . . say chariots?" I asked.

He looked at our hatch and said, "Not enough hold." He took a deep breath. "But something smaller, harnesses, decorations, maybe even that grain drink in amphorae or skins."

Bronze brooch.

He too was talking not of Massalia or Our Sea. (Only later did I realize that he was thinking not of the promised pentekonter but this gaulos.) He went on. "Trade is where you find it. Who knows what cargo I might take from Massalia, or where? A trader is a nomad. Only after he is rich can he think or do any other way."

He turned from the rail and called forward and aloft, "See anything?" Our conversation was over.

I studied Jason's long, dark head and short, wiry body. I could believe his ancestors invented the curved saber. Yet Tartessans were known as a serious, happy people. A legend has their laws written in verse, all now destroyed, and that they had traded from Hellenic shores north and west to most distant coasts. Now I wanted this man to achieve for himself and his men, and in memory of those ancestors, a measure of Tartessan greatness.

As I should have known, euphoria had to end. Late that afternoon, with Jason himself concerned about a rising cold northerly wind, Eban shouted from the masthead, "Ship astern!"

"What ship?"

"Rowing and sailing, moving fast! Like those Maurusians!"

Maurusians or Carthaginians – what difference? "Just what we need with a gale making up!" Jason climbed to Eban's perch.

The gale was already growing, out of the northwest under clear, dry skies – Our Sea's cold argestes which could blow for days. I knew how violent it could be, but felt our gaulos would ride it out – if our pursuers could be eluded.

The crew stowed and lashed gear. The men already had set up any slack standing rigging. Jason ordered extra lines to the sails, intending not to shorten sail unless he had to. I hoped our weathered sails could stand it.

Herakles joined Typhis at the lee steering oar, now bending in the increasingly heavy seas. The two were soon sweating while the rest of us shivered in this taste of coming winter. Eban had to come down from the jerking masthead, and told us the ship still gained.

"Carthaginian," Jason said. "He smells our blood."

Yet we were not to be overtaken easily. As heavy weather as we made of it, the Carthaginian, low-built and narrow, gained more and more slowly. It was built for fighting ships, not seas.

Once when both ships were on crests, I thought I could see several of his oars gone, either broken or brought back aboard, and men bailing water out the oarports and over the rail.

"Hope he swamps," Jason said.

We were now well past Meloussa and other islands of the west, and in about the widest part of Our Sea. We probably were due south of Massalia and being pushed toward the Libyan coast, though Jason also was fighting to move us farther eastward, even with the pirate hiding places of Ichnussa and Alalia ahead.

"Pirates won't be out in this," he said. "I hope."

Our argestes is never to be fooled with. Both ships were in trouble, although we at least seemed to be holding up well. The Carthaginian, usually safe in port in gales, rolled and pitched and gained no more on us. Nor could we shake him off. He was several stadia to weather, thus in better position whenever the gale moderated.

A strong gust hit him and we heard a faint explosion. "There goes his sail!" Jason exclaimed. Our men instinctively slacked ours before the gust got to us, but not enough. Ours too was quickly shredded.

Now we were equal, though the Carthaginian could put a score or more men to the oars when the time came. Yet ours were free men, theirs slaves with nothing to gain.

We drifted. Jason put the heavy ropes over the stern and we swung to a southerly heading. The Carthaginian did likewise.

For two days – the nights under a bright moon that gave us no help – we lay hove to, our men watching them, they watching us. Leonidas found ways to get us at least bread and cheese, but we felt the cold terribly. We slept little, Jason not at all. Our wounded man, weak and feverish, lay in the hold, with Leonidas helping him as much as he could. "His wound is festering," Leonidas told us after one visit below. He bathed the wound frequently in sea water but needed a healing balm from ashore.

The gale grew worse, still northwest. Here the seas had their longest fetch and built up almost like those on Okeanos – except so much closer together. We rose to crests and fell to troughs, as on that wild night off Iberia.

The gaulos groaned and creaked. Our mast began to sway with slacking of stays in the endless whip. I helped pull when the men tried to set them up again, but the ropes now stretched as fast as slack was taken up, and would not last long. Our forestay stranded, sure to part with a next violent plunge and jerk.

Herakles, a lifeline about his naked body, blue with cold, tried to brace the mast but Jason quickly saw even Herakles could hold it but a short time from the slick deck. Jason sent Eban for another line from the hold. Jason reached for it, but Eban himself scrambled up the ladder with the middle of the line. Jason saw what he was trying to do and quickly caught the ends and handed them to others, including me. Eban looped the middle about the mast-top. He came down safely and Jason was relieved. I knew Jason himself had planned to do any mast-top work. We pulled the ends taut and lashed them to the rail forward, and we were out of that trouble at least.

This went on hour after hour and seemed likely to go on day after day. We had lesser crises. Our oars had been lashed on deck, but two broke loose and jumped about as if alive, free to smash somebody's skull if not caught. I grabbed one before it did any damage, but had to let it go overside. The other hit a crewman's leg before Ogg fell on it. The man could not get up, his leg broken. Ogg lashed him to a stanchion in a protected spot, to suffer with his pain and the cold until Leonidas could help him.

With our troubles, Jason still took seconds often to look at the Carthaginian. It was still there. "Not much freeboard," Jason said to me.

He sent Leonidas below to see if we were taking water. We were, too much. Tired Herakles and three others went down and the giant soon was passing up amphorae to be dumped on deck. "Seams starting," Jason said.

The third day came and went, leaving us again in cold, bright moonlight. Jason, weary for sleep as well as from his labors, but still alert, looked northward at the sky. "Not tomorrow," he said. "Too much of this and sailors start doing things wrong."

Dawn brought no let-up. The wind if anything was stronger. All of us not needed on deck helped bail the hold. All were haggard, even young Eban. I suppose I was too, though my labors were less than Jason's or the men's. All were red-eyed, and older men had trouble keeping tight grips on ropes. Leonidas, ever faithful to his work, found food, often only soaked, salty crusts, but sustaining. He also tended the wounded man in the hold, now joined by the man with the broken leg. Leonidas had made rude splints and set the leg the best he could. The man had been silent in what had to be torture.

That night the wind began to abate. At dawn Jason looked about the ragged horizon.

"He's gone," he said, mostly to himself.

"Who?" I was startled.

"The Carthaginian. I saw him in the moonlight an hour ago."

"Maybe we drifted apart." I stared there and saw nothing, though in the still heaving seas I could have missed a ship as big as Mount Olympus.

"Maybe." He turned and smiled. "Maybe not."

He climbed the mast and looked all around. We still pitched and rolled, and Jason was snapped about. He came down.

"We can go home."

A broken oar drifted by.

"That's what's left."

The men cheered, hoarsely. I joined. Leonidas shouted down the hatch. Herakles cheered and handed up another amphora.

Jason had the storm sail put up and the steadying ropes over the stern brought aboard as the sun rose.

The wind eased, and in a few hours we were under full sail in an easterly apeliotes, our prow pointed north.

XXIV

THE LAST COURSE

JASON AND HALF THE CREW SLEPT, though not until he had looked in all directions for any new pursuer, Carthaginian or Maurusian. Jason and all awoke without being called for their watch. We sailed on, homeward.

A weary Herakles was told to go back to sleep, and he did at once, his loud snores bothering no one. The bailing went on, though with less urgency. The hold was getting clear. Late the second day Eban came up to report the water about gone.

"Easier going and the seams tighten up," Jason said. "Still we'll have to haul and re-calk right away."

Once Jason ordered the mainsail down for a ship on the eastern horizon, but whoever was there was as doubtful of us. He quickly dropped below the horizon and Jason raised our main and resumed course. Later we spoke a Sicilian trading vessel bound for Syracuse, asking if he had come from Massalia and knew a course there. (All our drifting in the gale had left us uncertain.) He had not but was glad to get Jason's story of the Carthaginian ship. "He says he thinks one of his warships is somewhere close and he'll pass it on. They are at war, you know."

About nightfall of the tenth day from the Pillars, Eban called from the bow. Land was in sight. Jason, Ogg, and I went forward. There was the dim line of the Galatic Gulf's northern shore. We could not pick out landmarks, and Jason shortened sail to slow us. The big harvest moon, now just past full, helped us, but Jason kept us moving only slowly. "If I see a harbor entrance, we can go in," he said. "If not, we will wait for daylight. I think we are west of Massalia."

Morning again confirmed his feel for the sea and the coast. We were off the Massaliot trading station of Narbo, not far from Rhodai, our first stop on our way west.

The apeliotes kept us from sailing for Massalia, but it was light and Jason put the men to the oars. Slowly we moved along our familiar coast, with Jason pointing out landmarks to Ogg. Eban, at his after oar, listened closely, and now and then missed a stroke trying to see where Jason was pointing.

"Let me take Eban's oar," I urged Jason. He nodded and I sent Eban to the poop. I was glad to get exercise, for since the argestes I had had little to do but sleep. I found that rowing was a skill and I too missed strokes until I got into the swing. Herakles, on the other side with me, helped me into an easier rhythmic motion. I gladly quit when Eban returned after an hour.

It was hours after midnight, under the bright moon, that Jason sighted marks for the Massalia harbor. We had been able to sail again with a change in the wind, but we would make no triumphal daylight return. We glided in with little sound except the soft singing of the men at the oars. Girondas was not here, but they knew their songs and Leonidas had led them before Girondas.

We came to Pasias' long quay and Jason eased our gaulos between two other craft, one the new pentekonter. Typhis steered deftly and with less than a cubit at either end, we touched neither ship. Oars were shipped, lines made fast, sails furled tightly, and the men told to rest. In our sick bay, the two men awoke, then slept again when Leonidas told them we were in harbor. The man with the spear gash had survived infection and was recovering, though a tendon must have been cut and he would never pull an oar again. The other would limp the rest of his life, but his leg was almost straight in the splints. Leonidas' healing skills matched his cooking skills – and his many others.

I was for leaping ashore. Jason pointed to Arktos. "You will stir up dogs and frighten your family. Two hours and it will be daylight."

He and all the others found their pallets and slept. I lay down, sure I would not sleep. I did not know how much I had taken on the ways of sailors. Jason shook me awake with the sun up when I could have sworn to Apollo I had not closed my eyes.

"Run or you will never explain yourself!" Jason laughed.

I took my bundle of gifts in one hand and the roll of journal and maps in the other and ran.

"Tell Pasias I will see him later," I called back.

Jason and the men waved me on.

My welcome at home was all a man could wish. It was broken only when I remembered I must report to the Aesymnète.

"Business," Anticlea smiled, "always business. Don't men know anything else?"

"This time, my love, I will be back before another leaf falls."

XXV

A WORLD SHAKEN

I WAS NETTLED when I finally saw the Aesymnète. Others rushed in and out of his chamber. I hoped no garbled report of our voyage had preceded us. I expected no hero's welcome, but thought he might have taken at least a moment to greet me.

He did seem weary and preoccupied. Had he forgotten?

"You must excuse me," he said at last. "Much has happened."

"We are not at war?" I asked, alarmed.

"No, thank Zeus and all other gods, even Ares, but while you were gone we had news from Babylon. Alexander is dead."

I started. I tried to think what this meant. We were Greeks, but nearly his most remote subjects, if subjects at all.

"In battle?" I asked.

"In bed," he sighed. "Malaria. It was the twenty-eighth day of Daesius."

A week before solstice! We were racing up the Haemodae! Our best discoveries still to come, and at home our world was shaking!

"Pytheas, I want to talk to you, and at length," the Aesymnète said. "I am sure you and your Tartessans achieved all we sent you for and more. But today is not the day. I wish birds could have flown ahead to tell us you were coming, though that would not have stayed history already made. We cannot guess what this will do to our comfortable little world.

"I am sure there is little mourning at Athens, but there is so much chicanery and corruption there that it's no place for support or enlightenment. Even Demosthenes fined and exiled for taking a bribe in that messy Harpalos affair last year! Perikles and Sokrates would shudder. Rome and Carthage no doubt are jubilant, even if they have other fights on their hands now. Massalia indeed would be a prize."

He stared out the window. Men and boats moved in our harbor, men and carts on our streets. The fall sky was blue, the air good. Nothing seemed changed.

"The Timuques meet again now. They have met almost every day. You may want to hear what they say and decide, if anything."

"I will take no more of your time," I said. Impatient men were standing outside, and a runner had come in often to hand him a message or a scroll.

He embraced me and I left. The Timuques were gathering. Many had concerned looks, some solemn. I saw Meton and Pasias in the crowd and went to them.

"Pytheas!" Meton exclaimed. "Pasias said your ship was in."

"And at what a time," I said.

"The chief has told you, then."

"We just talked a few minutes. He has much on his mind."

"So do we all, though you'd think we'd know what to do by now, as long as we've been shouting about it."

"I will just ask one thing," I said hurriedly amid the din. "Jason must have showed you our cassiterite and elektron. And I have a gold nugget from Ierné. What shall we do with it all?"

"That cargo has been unloaded," Pasias said. "It is yours and the Tartessans'. We will see that you get what it is worth. Meton and I will buy the cassiterite and elektron ourselves. You make your own deal on the nugget."

"But, isn't it all the city's?"

"Pytheas," Meton laughed, "don't let civic virtue overwhelm good sense. You and Jason and the men took all the risk and suffered all the hardships and I am sure there were many. If anybody owns that cargo, you do. Now if you don't want to listen to us argue futilities, go to the yard and divide up shares – so much for Jason, so much for each sailor, so much for you. And don't be unselfish – you have a wife and children!"

I went out. We have enough debates among our scientists, and debates too often make only for more confusion, with the debaters more intent on scoring as in an Olympic contest than in truth. I walked to Pasias' shipyard.

There on the quay was our cargo. Off the ship it seemed small. I looked over the ingots and ore and elektron. I asked why we had worked so hard and risked so much for such dead things, then remembered that men had always done so.

Jason and the men were on the deck, busy as usual but in no haste. Stretched along the deck was the rusty ten-cubit chain length Herakles had filched from the Veneti.

"Have you talked to Pasias?" I asked. "Are you going to have the pentekonter?"

"No," Jason replied.

"But he said, the city said you could."

"This gaulos is a sweet little ship," Jason smiled. "It is just right for us. With the pentekonter, I would not be a captain, I would be a clerk. I would have to keep hundreds of pieces of papyrus, so much of this, so much of that, where is it in the hold? I would have to find money for many men's wages and listen to many men's troubles. I would have to take strangers' words for what I could not see. I would have to deal with more thieves than honest men."

"But the pentekonter would make you rich."

"Maybe. I never see a rich man happy. Rich Carthaginians cry because they think somebody else is richer. Here Pasias and Meton worry all the time. No, I will keep the gaulos. My only worry will be keeping away from Carthaginians and pirates."

"Did you hear the news?"

"Alexander? Yes. It's all over the taverns. We heard a woman named Medius got him drunk two weeks earlier to start his fever. And his Roxana was already large with his prince."

"The Aesymnète did not mention that."

"He should go to the taverns."

"Do you have any guess what this means—for Massalia?"

"Ask your gods—their guess will be no wilder than mine."

Here I could only remember Meton's and Pasias' wine-table conversation a year ago. Yet then Meton had feared Alexander's own urge to conquer. Now would it be the obverse? Would Rome or Syracuse or Carthage set out? The Aesymnète seemed to fear that. I supposed he knew enough of world affairs. I did not.

"Let your Timuques figure it out," Jason added. "We have to get the gaulos ready. Pasias has chartered us for a cargo to Alexandria, then to Italy in the spring—if the world is still in one piece."

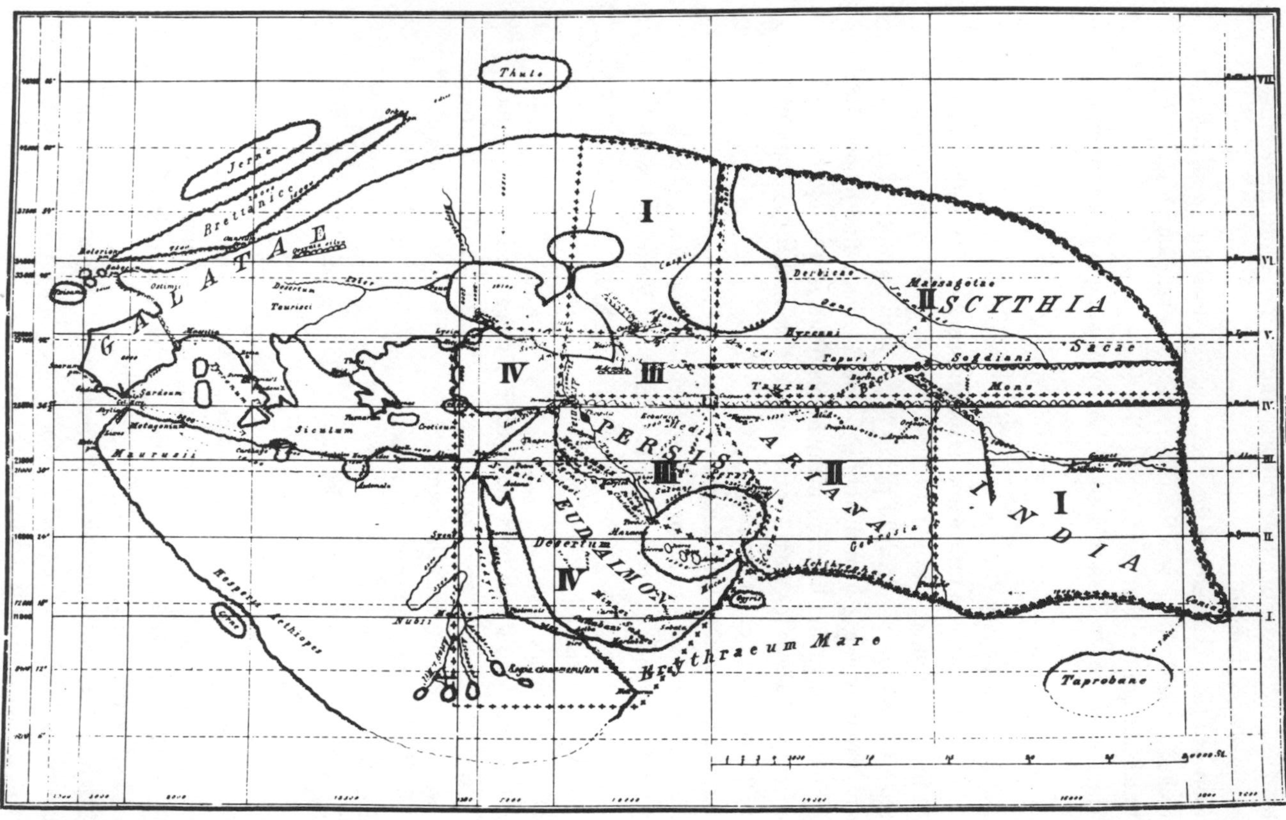

The world according to Eratosthenes.

"Maybe our own affairs are all we can take care of," I said. "For one thing, Pasias and Meton say we are to share in what we brought back. How do you work that out?"

"My men say equal shares for all."

"And Ogg."

"Yes, he has earned it."

"But you, Jason, you led us. You should get more."

"Don't worry about me. I get the gaulos."

"Well, then, how many shares do you count?"

"There are twelve of us, and you."

"I am rich with what I have learned. But I will take a share or my Anticlea will scold without mercy. Thirteen?"

"Sixteen–three for the ship. We have to buy stores and replace rigging, sails, rope, and other gear. She will have to be hauled to have the bottom cleaned. She needs paint. There is another soft plank. And all that re-calking."

"You are already a businessman," I said. "You might as well have the pentekonter."

Jason laughed and shook his head.

XXVI

WHAT CAME OF IT

I WISH I COULD REPORT now that Massalia made good use of what we found and learned. It would be nice to report that my Academy colleagues, Aristotle's Peripatetics in declining Athens, or the rising scholars in Alexandria found my discoveries, and all that Jason and his Tartessans had taught me, at least interesting.

This I cannot do. Whether to blame all these people or just history, I do not know.

Alexander's death changed Massalia's whole perspective. The world around Our Sea swung between chaos and tight order imposed for a while by Alexander's generals, his Diadochi, his satraps.

Affecting me more directly was the death a year later of Aristotle. While he had his prejudices, he was more open-minded than any of our Greek thinkers. Whether he knew of our voyage I never learned.

Times were troubled for him. His past intellectual sponsorship of Alexander weighed against him in Athens' emotional reaction to the death of the conqueror. Alexander had strayed from much that Aristotle taught him but Athens still thought of both as of one mind. Athens further cherished its hatred of the Persians, and Alexander had sought an empire embracing both.

None of this endeared Aristotle to Athenians. He fled to his mother's home at Chalcis on Euboea, to die, not of old age for he was only sixty-two years old, more likely of heartbreak.

How much if at all Dicaearchus and other Peripatetics read later of my *Peri tou Okeanou* I never heard. They were hostile. Aristotle's Earth, Air, Fire, and Water were all they cared to know about.

Later I took a copy to Alexandria. I went with Jason and the Tartessans on the gaulos, which Pasias kept busy. It was good to relive the life of our voyage to the edge of the ice, if only for a week under our summer sun.

At Alexandria I found satrap Ptolemy, now called Soter, had established, as promised, a library, growing and attracting scholars. It was becoming an academy like Massalia's, even like Aristotle's Lyceum. I felt that here, not Athens, must be the future of science and philosophy.

My contribution was welcomed, and I got to describe our adventures. I brought Jason to one meeting to add navigational detail. A number of Egyptian captains questioned us closely – more closely than the scholars. Thc Egyptians did not, however, think to the west. As with the scholars, Our Sea and all that lay east, and south along the Nile, was their world. One or two still cherished a dream of redigging Queen Hatshepsut's ancient canal to the Arabian Gulf!

Mathematicians and astronomers were interested in my latitude calculations. Yet the concern was with application in the world they knew, the same world as the captains'.

What else in those busy months after we returned? I had a long talk with our Aesymnète during a lull in the commotion over Alexander. He had read my *Peri tou Okeanou.*

"You have told us much, Pytheas," the Aesymnète said. "It is up to us to profit by it."

Again he looked out on the harbor. "I make you no promises," he continued. "As you must know, many opposed the whole thing. I guess they thought I was going to make something out of it, or that Meton or Pasias would. Now they say, 'What of it?' They read only enough of your report to see the ice and the storms and the strange people, the 'barbarians.' But be patient with us. Even I cannot say do this or do that. And the Timuques, they will talk anything to death. Much eloquence, little decision."

The Aesymnète had me address the Timuques. Except from Meton and Pasias and their friends, there was calm interest at best. One Timuque asked how often we could hope to get past the Pillars of Herakles. That was a question for a general, and none offered to answer. True, we had only one Jason, and even his luck and skill had almost failed.

The attitude seemed to be, "Let well enough alone." To me as a scientist, it was galling. But I did have to remember that we were sent with trade first in mind, and I myself had found that our cassiterite and elektron already came to us the shortest and easiest way, whatever the cost.

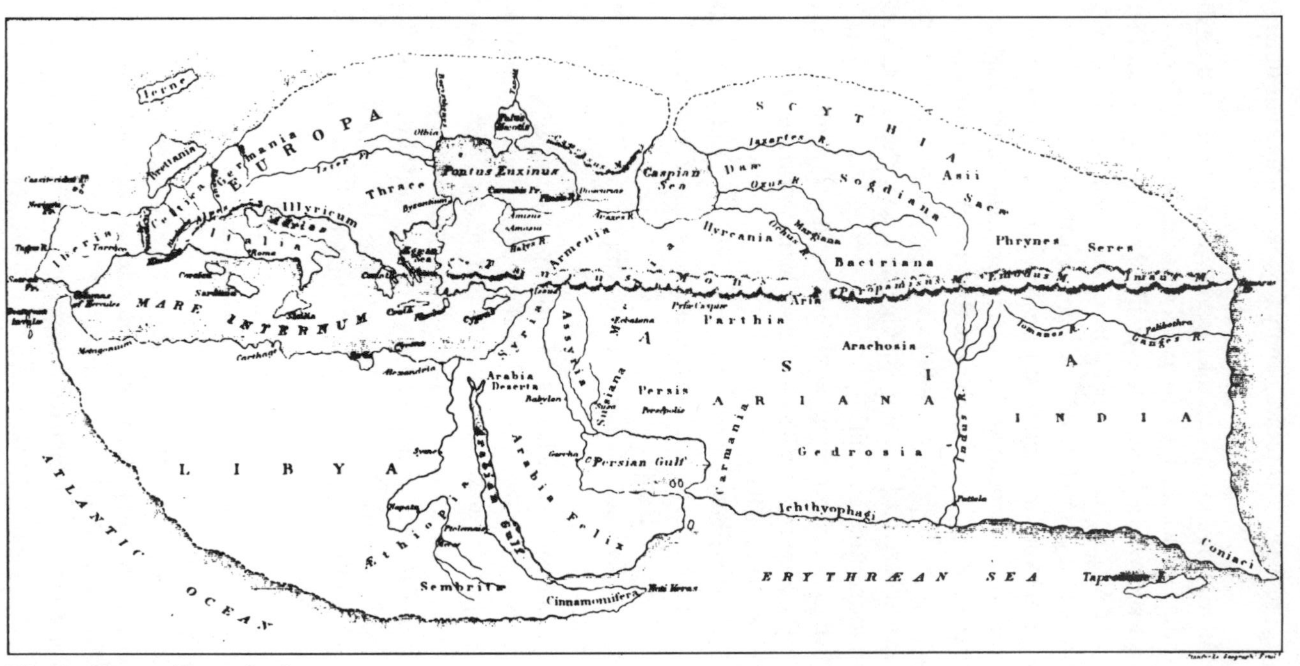

The world according to Strabo.

The Timuques passed a resolution thanking me, praising me for all the new astronomical and geographical knowledge, assuring me of an intent to use all for the betterment of mankind and of Massalia, committing themselves to nothing. A scroll was ordered drawn up by a calligrapher, to be presented to me.

They then turned to regular business, including hearing the latest from Rome and Carthage. Sooner or later, the Timuques must decide which – if either – to favor in the struggle for supremacy on Our Sea.

Meton came to me at home after the session.

"Maybe the chief was wrong to push this last year," he said. "I should have known that Masssalia was not ready. But who knew that Alexander was to die so soon? A young man, impossible to stop. His enemies were not stupid. He was just too smart. But a fever got him, just as it gets any beggar in the agora. Never mind that he should have stayed with his Roxana instead of carousing with that other woman. If all of us got what we deserved, there would not be enough islands for exile or executioners to feed us to the crows."

I told him I had no regrets, except for Massalia.

"I learned more in six months than most men hope to in a lifetime," I said. "I have food for study for the rest of my life. I may come upon answers to questions no man has answered yet. Or I may make it possible for some other man. I am grateful to you and Pasias and the Aesymnète and all."

"Don't be reasonable," Meton smiled. "I feel like going out and kicking, myself or somebody else, and I have nominations."

I still had a little of the Veneti wine from the Sequana. I poured cups and said, "It is not like yours, but you ought to get at least a taste of something from our voyage."

He sipped the cup. "Veneti, you say?" He sipped again and rolled the wine about his mouth. "I could teach them something. I guess they could teach me something, too. They must have fine grapes up there. And the wine must travel well."

"Yours traveled farther and as well – almost to Thule and then to Samland. And remember, the Veneti are not so far from here – straight northwest across Keltika."

"Ah, yes, that's the line we hoped to shorten the long way, isn't it? Well, here's to the Veneti and their elektron and their cassiterite. I guess that's the way things will be for a while."

XXVII

JASON'S FAREWELL

I WAS IN MY STUDY, trying to remember details now less clear, when I heard Dryas and Anthia making a joyous commotion in the courtyard, Anticlea's greeting, then a familiar voice.

"Jason!" The children and Anticlea always welcomed him.

It was spring, a year and a half later. He was just back from Italy. My own joy was twofold: We talked as friends and he could clarify my now cold notes. His observations and memory were often truer. And I wanted to try a few of my theories: Was the tide influenced by solstice as well as the moon? How did the moon pull up these masses of water – if it did . . . as it must? How about heights? We had seen tides washing up high cliffs. Did he think tides influenced the lives of people living near? Why were tides so great there and where they wrecked Alexander's fleet in the Erythraean Sea, yet so little on Our Sea?

What did he think was in the Gulf of Metuonis which congealed to make so much elektron? Scholars at our Academy, familiar with the scant supplies found on Our Sea, had asked me.

He gave me his thoughts, all practical, all helpful. At last I let him tell all he had done since his last visit. His merchant voyage had been successful. No unusual troubles. "Carthaginians I met asked if I knew what had become of one of their galleys in that worst of argestes that time. I told the truth. I never heard what happened to it." The gaulos was all he expected. His crew, reliable and strong except for the two now crippled men, worked it well, the two handling lighter duties. Eban shared the steering oars with Typhis and Ogg. Herakles, his beard now gray to white, was thinking of retiring to open a tavern here with his grain brew. "We all have to leave the sea some day," Jason said, "or risk our bones washing up on some far-off beach for wolves to gnaw."

His face became concerned. What was going on in Our Sea? How much longer could a free merchant operate and not be impressed into battle? To Carthage he would always be of a slave race. Sicily and Etruria and Rome might not always recognize his rights as a new Massaliot citizen. He would not risk being trapped in the Euxine, whence other traders brought rich goods. He wanted no fortune.

"And what is happening with the merchants of Massalia?"

I knew, a little. With the growing importance of Ptolemy's Alexandria, and eastern lands now under Macedonian and Greek rule, trade looked east. Massalia was building ships. Never had Pasias' yard and others been so busy! Rome needed our ships most, to haul grain from Libya to its growing cities.

"Didn't you think your leaders would take an interest in the north, even put trading posts in Pritania or Iernê or Abalus? There's more than cassiterite and elektron to trade in."

I shook my head. I had so hoped, even knowing the cassiterite and elektron trades could not change. I had tried to tell the Academy, the Forum, and the Timuques of the beauty of the great northern island, and of other opportunities. But the money was to be made to the east.

"I think I'll try it myself," Jason said. "I may even stay. There I am a free man."

This I knew had long bothered him. He had known his status in Our Sea—what his Tartessan people had lived with for nearly two hundred years. I wanted to keep him here. Ironically, I had been the one to show him a different world. Even as my Ionian ancestors had fled Phocaea westward from Medes and Persians, he would be going to a new land where a man could stand on his own worth, a Tartessan the peer of Pritani, Abalans, Gutones, Teutoni, even Veneti.

Our world was torn by rivalries likely to grow. My family and I were safe. But what of my work? In times of strife, the only knowledge wanted is of making war machines. Who cared about the northern coasts of Europe now? Jason had just told what could happen to the individual.

I would miss him, and envy him a little, a man of all the men I had ever known, with whom I would rather spend my time, and exchange ideas.

All I could say to him was, "Jason, you are the equal or better than any man I have ever known."

He shook his head. "That's to be proved." He looked away. The way his mouth tightened I thought of something more wonderful to him than freedom, on a shore of those northern waters. How could I forget her? I had been so sure Tregela would marry in a neighboring kingdom! I had given her no more thought—I had my Anticlea.

"Go prove it!" I said, slapping him on the back. How wonderful to be in love! Now, I wanted to hurry him on his way. My theory, "nothing happens by chance," applied here, as well as in astronomy.

But he wasn't ready to tell his own affairs. I asked if he planned to see Tregela, but all he said was, "She might need help if that drunken uncle shows up again. Herakles should have held him under." I went back to generalities.

"Can you get by the Pillars again? The Carthaginians must have long memories."

"There will be moonless nights."

"Do you think you can get along with the Veneti?"

"I think I can manage. Some could be my cousins."

"But we thought of them as villains!"

"Not quite. Sharp. Aggressive. But you know that when the Tartessans were conquered, some fled north. Others put to sea—at least those in ships outside the harbor. Carthage conquered us by sneaking down the coastal mountain valleys and attacking from land. We like to think it is the inheritance of our wits that has made the Veneti the great seamen they are."

"Well," said I, "nobody told me that before. But it is logical."

"We had a beautiful city. Some stayed on, hoping to recover. Over two hundred years many have slipped away. Where else would they go?"

"And now you."

"And now I go."

"Good luck."

FOR FURTHER READING

THE PYTHEAS STORY can be explored through books, articles, and lectures of the past century and before. A beginning might be a translation of Strabo's geographical writings, either in the Loeb Classical Library or the H. C. Hamilton – W. Falconer volumes (London: Bell, 1903). Strabo is the wellspring for almost everything concerning Pytheas.

Sir Edward H. Bunbury's *A History of Ancient Geography* (1879) has been republished (New York: Dover, 1959), and Sir Clements R. Markham's "Pytheas, the Discoverer of Britain" appeared in London's *Geographical Journal* in 1893. C. F. C. Hawkes' lecture, "Pytheas: Europe and the Greek Explorers," which can be found in some libraries, is scholarly and contentious, almost to the point of confusion for anyone just wanting the story.

If you read French, and can find it among rare books, M. D. A. Azuni's *Mémoires,* which we cite in our introduction, can tell you much about Pytheas and Massalia. (The Mariners' Museum library in Newport News, Va., has the only copy we have located.) Raoul Busquet's *Histoire de Marseille* (Paris: Editions Robert Laffont, 1945) is also very helpful.

Max Carey and E. H. Warmington's *The Ancient Explorers* (1929) was republished by Penguin in 1963. E. H. Warmington's *Greek Geography* (London: Dent, 1934) and B. H. Warmington's *Carthage* (London: R. Hale, 1960) should be read, briefly at least, along with William Culican's *The First Merchant Venturers* (New York: McGraw-Hill, 1966) and J. V. Luce's essay on early exploration in Geoffrey Ashe's *Quest for America* (New York: Praeger, 1971).

Rhys Carpenter's works, including *The Greeks in Spain* (London: Longmans Green, 1925) and *Beyond the Pillars of Heracles* (New York: Delacorte, 1966), leave little unexamined. Pierson Dixon's *The Iberians in Spain* (London: Oxford, 1940) gives further background.

If you can stand today's condescension, read also Will Durant's *The Life of Greece* (New York: Simon & Shuster, 1949) and Edith Hamilton's

The Greek Way (New York: Norton, 1930). They will be enjoyed long after many of today's historians have gone to well-earned oblivion.

The story of Tartessos, which we have joined to our account of Pytheas, can be read in full in Ellen Mary Whishaw's *Atlantis in Andalucia* (London: Rider, 1929). Today, Mrs. Whishaw would be considered "a little old lady in tennis shoes," not a professional archeologist or historian. She was the wife of an engineer for Río Tinto Mines, exploiting the rich zinc, copper and silver veins of Andalucía's Huelva-Palos-Niebla country. She spent years in the 1920s and earlier exploring, especially in the ruined Tartessan fortress at Niebla on the Río Tinto, and gleaning "folk wisdom." Read the book, if you can find it short of the Library of Congress, to learn about a forgotten civilization. You don't have to accept her theory that Tartessans were refugees from Atlantis, though it's no more improbable than many another.

For descriptions of ancient ships and sailors, Lionel Casson's *Illustrated History of Ships and Boats* (Garden City: Doubleday, 1964) and *Ships and Seamanship in the Ancient World* (Princeton: Princeton University Press, 1971) will help you respect men and boats of millennia before fiberglass and loran. Likewise Edward Keble Chatterton's *Ships and Ways of Other Days* (London: Sidgwick & Jackson, 1913) and his many other writings on the history of shipbuilding, navigation, and sailing men.

There are scores of other books and articles on this whole pre-Christian scene. Your librarian can steer you, as they have steered us toward Huelva, Sevilla, and Barcelona, Spain; Penzance and Truro, Cornwall; Trinity College, Dublin; and our Library of Congress, the American Geographical Society at Milwaukee, the Richmond Public Library, the Mariners' Museum in Newport News, the Charles Taylor Library and Thomas Nelson Community College in neighboring Hampton, the College of William and Mary, and the Edgar Cayce Foundation in Virginia Beach (the latter for the only copy of the Whishaw book we know of in this country except in the Library of Congress). For calculations on probable moon phases so long ago, go to a planetarium like the one at Newport News' Peninsula Nature and Science Center.